The major purpose of this book is to open the eyes of Peak District visitors to the exciting pursuit in the open-air of the science of Geology.

The Peak District is a scenically attractive area with numerous pockets of outstanding beauty and, for the most part, is unsullied by the activities of man. Its rocks take us back hundreds of millions of years when the distribution of land and sea as well as climatic regimes were very different. Like all the major sciences, Geology, the study of the Earth, has ancient foundations and, though it now has its own sophisticated methods of research, the amateur can still make important discoveries whilst, at the same time, working in congenial surroundings.

The book is very largely a reprint of the author's 'Geology Explained in the Peak District', (David & Charles, 1976) which quickly went out-of-print. It has been brought up-to-date, and whilst it does not pretend to be a comprehensive account of the geology of the area it does explain the major principles of Geology through a carefully selected series of itineraries. The author hopes that the reader will follow some of these in the field and share with him the many joys of observation and discovery on and in the rocks.

The author is grateful to Dr David Mitchell of Scarthin Books for his courage and enthusiasm, which has led to this publication.

F. Wolverson Cope

Blackwell Dale,
Derbyshire.

May 1997

GEOLOGY EXPLAINED
IN THE
PEAK DISTRICT

by
F. WOLVERSON COPE, D.Sc., C.Eng., F.I.Min.E., F.G.S.
Emeritus Professor of Geology

Illustrations by
the Author

SCARTHIN BOOKS
Cromford, Derbyshire
1998

Published by Scarthin Books, Cromford, Derbyshire, 1998

Phototypesetting by Techniset Typesetters, Newton-le-Willows

Printed in Great Britain by Antony Rowe Ltd, Chippenham, Wiltshire

ISBN 0 907758 98 3

Contents

Introduction

The Peak District is an upland area of considerable diversity lying generally more than 300m above sea-level and covering the southern part of the Pennines in north-midland Britain. It lies mainly in the northern part of the county of Derbyshire, but physiographically and geologically it extends into the adjacent counties of Cheshire, Staffordshire and Yorkshire (Figure 1).

The name 'Peak District' conjures up visions of sharp or even spiky hills and mountains, and to this extent it is barely appropriate. The area was referred to as *Peaclond* as early as the year AD 924 according to the Anglo-Saxon Chronicle. The word 'peak' is derived from the Old English *peac* meaning 'a hill or peak'. It could be maintained that the Peak District is by no means the most outstanding area in Britain for the occurrence of peaks, though if one were to exclude Scotland and Wales, and look at England alone, then it might claim this distinction. The English Lake District has much more striking mountains, but its numerous beautiful lakes give it a uniqueness in Britain which deservedly prescribes its name.

The Peak District is an area of contrasts scenically, geologically, and culturally. Centrally, there is an upland plateau of limestones and some volcanic rocks cut by gorge-like valleys, some with rivers but others dry, surmounted by castellated limestone cliffs, the plateau surface being largely grassland criss-crossed by white-weathering dry-stone walls and with scattered plantations, mainly of beech. Small farms abound. Peripherally there is higher more mountainous country often reaching to 600m above sea-level, composed of sandstones and shales often covered with a thick mantle of peat, traversed by deep and sometimes sombre valleys overlooked by cliffs and crags of brown-weathering sandstone; here and there are dark-coloured dry-stone walls behind which

7

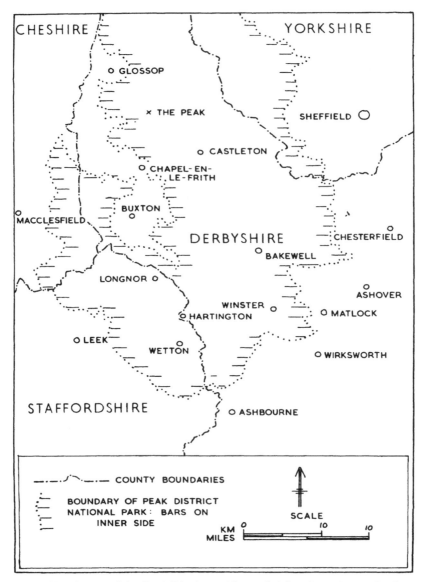

Fig 1   Sketch-map of the Peak District and immediately adjacent areas to show limits of Peak District National Park and county boundaries. *Crown Copyright reserved*

sheep huddle for shelter from fierce winter storms of rain and snow.

It is an area of great natural beauty where colour varies extra-ordinarily with the seasons, affording relaxation and opportunity for imagination for thousands of country-loving people, especially for those who live just outside its boundaries in the conurbations of Manchester, Sheffield, Stoke-on-Trent, and Derby.

Thinking travellers through the Peak District during the Middle Ages, struck by the depths of some of its valleys and the often precipitous nature of their sides, supposed that these natural features must have been formed by intense catastrophe. Even today, the notion of catastrophic change and of spontaneous creation is remarkably widespread, be it to account for natural gorges or for the occurrence of maggots in cheese. It is probably more persistent than superstition. No doubt the general ignorance over the evolution of landscapes is due to a lack of appreciation of the importance and the immensity of time.

Many a visitor to a beauty spot in the limestone part of the Peak District must notice shapes and objects in the limestone which remind him vividly of shells he has seen on a sea-shore, and wonder how they came to be embedded in solid rocks. Similarly, he can not fail to notice that many of the rocks are built up of layers of varying thickness sometimes lying horizontally like a giant's pack of cards (Figure 2), in other cases inclined or even bent or folded (Figure 3).

Pyramidal hills are not uncommon in some parts of the Peak District; the shape reminds many travellers of postcard views of Vesuvius or Cotapaxi, and without further evidence it is often assumed that these hills were formed by volcanic action, again catastrophic. Even today, many children are inculcated at school with the catastrophic idea when they are taught that mountains have been 'thrust up' or are the results of 'upheaval'. Such misconceived ideas can certainly arise when there is a lack of appreciation of the time factor. It is true, as we shall see later in this book, that volcanic action enters into the long history of parts of the Peak District, but with rare exceptions the volcanic rocks do not give rise to hills.

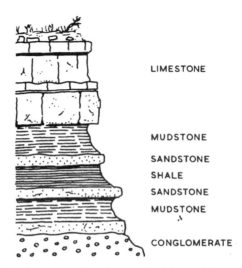

LIMESTONE

MUDSTONE

SANDSTONE

SHALE

SANDSTONE

MUDSTONE

CONGLOMERATE

Fig 2   Bedding in horizontal sedimentary rocks. The notation of shading for the different lithologies is used in all diagrams

Fig 3   Small anticlinal fold in thin sandstones and shales (Lower Namurian), Wildboarclough, Cheshire. From a sketch made in 1926

Possibly since Roman times and to a vastly increasing extent in the last two hundred years, many naturally occurring materials, rocks and minerals, have been dug, quarried or mined in the Peak District. They include ores of lead and zinc, and even of copper, as well as barytes and fluor-spar; the last named is still being worked on an appreciable scale. In various places the old mine-hillocks still yield good specimens of minerals, and the collector soon appreciates that not all minerals occur in the same place, and that in some districts two or more minerals appear to be closely associated.

Coal seams also occur in the rocks on the western fringes of the Peak District. If these really do represent the vegetation of tropical forests there must be some explanation for the shift of climatic zones. There is abundant evidence that the whole of the Earth was by no means warm at the time when coal seams were formed in some regions.

All these are matters embranced by the science of geology. Stated briefly, geology is the science of the Earth, the history of the Earth and its inhabitants. Naturally this history must be based upon the rocks, the materials of which the Earth is made, and this is why all geological work must be founded upon sound and detailed field-work. With the advance of knowledge, geology in common with the other sciences, now employs sophisticated equipment and methods. Fortunately, a great deal of basic fieldwork can be carried out with very simple and inexpensive equipment. The keen amateur, who has learned the principles, and who has taught himself to observe and record accurately and precisely can, working in an attractive region like the Peak District, obtain great personal satisfaction and enjoyment and, at the same time, contribute to the elucidation of the geological history of the area.

The main aims of this book are to demonstrate some of the more important principles of geology in the Peak District, to explain how the geologist interprets and explains what he sees, and to explain the landscape and life of the area in the light of its geology. Terms are generally explained as they are introduced, but a Glossary is included at the end of the book to simplify reference. Beginners often experience difficulty in geological chronology so that a Table of geological time including the chronology of Peak District rocks is given for reference (Appendix I).

The rocks, fossils, and minerals of the Peak District attracted the author to the study of geology at the early age of eleven years. For nearly seventy years he has carried out research on various aspects of Peak District geology, and still recalls the excitement and fascination of first discovery. He writes this book in the hope that readers may be able to share this experience in one of the most beautiful parts of Great Britain.

CHAPTER 1

Geology in the Field

Many people are attracted to the study of geology because it is essentially a field science, and may be carred out in pleasant country surroundings. For the amateur and for many professional geologists this is usually likely to be the case, though many professionals spend a great deal of their time in inhospitable or in uncomfortable surroundings, amid ice or in the heat of arid deserts, in tropical swamps, or in mines.

The precise methods to be adopted in the field depend very largely upon whether one is an amateur satisfying a natural curiosity, or a geologist working with specific aims in view. The nature of the terrain is another important factor.

The beginner will find gratification in going into an area and collecting specimens of minerals, rocks, and fossils for later study at home; he will quickly progress to observing the broad structure of rocks, and the kind of relationship between this structure and the main features of the landscape. He may, for example, quickly find reasons for a particular hill having an asymmetric shape, very steep on one side and gently sloping on the other, or for a waterfall being present in one particular part of a stream and not in another.

FIELD EQUIPMENT

The equipment required at this stage is simple and inexpensive:

A geological hammer, about a kilogram in weight, the head being square at one end and chisel-shaped at the other. The hammer is used for removing the weathered skin of a rock in order to examine a fresh and unweathered surface, or to collect specimens.

A pocket-lens, preferably with a magnification of ten.

A pocket-knife, for testing the hardness of minerals or for splitting finely laminated muddy rocks, shales.

A one-inch Ordnance Survey map of the area, and a one-inch Geological Survey map of the area, or their metric equivalents.

A small notebook of plain paper for notes and sketches.

A supply of wrapping paper, rubber bands, labels, etc for transport of specimens.

At a later stage, and particularly if original detailed work is to be attempted, the following would be added to the list:

A clinometer-compass to measure the amount and direction of dip of sedimentary rocks, joint and cleavage directions, and orientations of mineral veins, faults and folds.

Six-inch Ordnance Survey maps of the area for the recording of data in the field, or maps on the nearest metric scale.

A map-scale to read yards or metres according to the maps used. Pencils and eraser.

A steel tape preferably with a metric scale.

It is not the purpose of this chapter to tell the reader how to observe and what to observe; this is done in later chapters with reference to specific areas or exposures in the Peak District.

THE COUNTRYSIDE CODE

Those visiting the countryside for whatever purpose should observe the Countryside Code. Students of geology quickly find that they must leave roads and footpaths, enter private grounds, use farm gates or climb walls. In the Peak District, many walls built of limestone will collapse readily (limestone is slowly soluble in rain water and this causes instability), and great care is needed. The more important elements of this code are:

1   Do not leave any litter.
2   Do not light fires.

3 Obtain the permission of the farmer or landowner before crossing fields other than by public footpath, or before visiting quarries and other exposures off the beaten track.

4 Do not walk through meadow grass or trample crops.

5 Close all gates after passing through; if a field gate will not open, climb over it at the hinge end as this is less likely to cause damage.

6 Do not hammer rocks aimlessly; be careful not to damage an exposure, and do not collect more material than you need for serious study.

7 Do not leave rock fragments on footpaths or roads, and when working on an exposure alongside a main road be careful that pieces of rock do not roll into the path of vehicles.

8 Before you climb over a wall find out whether there is a gate or sheep-hole which would afford easier passage.

9 If you are compelled to climb a wall and stones are dislodged, replace them carefully before you leave.

10 Do not scare farm animals, especially sheep during the lambing season.

THE PEAK DISTRICT NATIONAL PARK AUTHORITY

A large part of the Peak District lies within the oversight of the Peak District National Park Authority. While this may make access somewhat easier, it does impose certain restrictions on collecting; in several specific areas such as the picnic area in Tideswell Dale, the collection of plants and rocks is strictly forbidden. The policy of the Peak District National Park Authority does not, however, preclude serious geological research, and it will give sympathetic consideration to any application to carry out specific research. The address of the Authority is Aldern House, Baslow Road, Bakewell, Derbyshire, DE4 1AE.

CHAPTER 2

Identifying Rocks, Minerals and Fossils

ROCKS

The accessible part of the Earth's crust is composed of rocks. To the layman the term 'rock' conveys a sense of hardness and durability, but to the geologist a rock is any aggregate of mineral particles. According to this simple scientific definition, therefore, soft sand or plastic clay is just as much a rock as a piece of granite.

Any rock may be placed in one of three major groups. *Igneous rocks* are those which have cooled from a state of fusion. Some igneous rocks may be witnessed in process of formation in active volcanoes at the present day, and such igneous rocks which are poured out or blown out explosively on to the surface of the Earth are known as volcanic or extrusive rocks. The most obvious ones are lavas which flow out of volcanic orifices and then cool and solidify. Some lavas are visibly crystalline but others, particularly those which have cooled very rapidly, are either so finely crystalline that this can only be seen under the microscope, or are non-crystalline and 'glassy'. Volcanic rocks, both lavas and ashes, occur in the Peak District, where they are associated with limestones.

The heated parent material which may rise to the surface to give rise to volcanic rocks and the liberation of gases and steam is known by the general term 'magma'. Volcanic activity is merely the surface manifestation of more extensive magmatic or igneous activity within the Earth's crust or in the outer part of the region beneath the crust known as the 'mantle'. Magma may force or melt its way into the crustal rocks to give rise to *intrusive igneous rocks*. As the magma normally cools slowly in this enclosed environment, these intrusive rocks usually show a well developed crystalline structure readily visible to the naked eye. The only intrusive rocks in the Peak District are relatively small bodies in which the rocks are not coarsely crystalline.

The second great group of rocks is the *sedimentary rocks*. Wherever rocks are exposed they are broken up by numerous agencies, frost, plant roots, running water, ice, chemical decomposition and so on. Under the action of gravity the broken particles becoming ever finer are carried to lower levels by rivers and in some cases the sea, so that ultimately the solid particles come to rest upon the beds of lakes or seas. The soluble salts produced by chemical decomposition of the crustal rocks are similarly transported and some are available to animals for the production of calcareous shells or carapaces and skeletal elements such as bones; such salts may also be precipitated by physical changes affecting the aqueous medium. All these materials derived from the denudation of pre-existing rocks give rise to sedimentary rocks. They are characterised by being bedded or stratified and by containing fossils.

In order that any considerable thickness of sediments may accumulate in a given area it is necessary that the Earth's crust should be subsiding. Any subsequent upward movement will inevitably result in the denudation of some of the newly deposited sediments.

Igneous rocks or sedimentary rocks which are changed in character by heat, pressure, or an alteration of chemical environment are known as *metamorphic rocks*. When sediments are subjected to metamorphism bedding may be obscured or eliminated, new structures may be superimposed, and any fossils present may be distorted or destroyed. The only metamorphic rocks in the Peak District are limestones which have been thermally altered by igneous intrusions.

Brief descriptions of the more commonly occurring rocks in the Peak District are given below.

Limestone A sedimentary rock, usually well bedded or stratified, and well jointed, consisting of calcium carbonate, $CaCO_3$, or calcium magnesium carbonate, $CaMg(CO_3)_2$. Limestones are being formed today in some seas by chemical precipitation or by biological processes; for example, many marine organisms secrete calcium carbonate from sea-water to produce a protective shell or 'test', and when the animals die these tests may accumulate to form a shelly limestone. The limestones of the Peak District are entirely of marine origin, the evidence being based mainly upon the types of fossil organisms they contain.

During or shortly after deposition highly calcareous rocks like limestones, still in contact with sea-water, may have some of the calcium carbonate replaced by magnesium carbonate to give a brown-weathering rock called a dolomitised limestone or, in cases of extensive replacement, a dolomite.

Limestones may be of many colours; almost white when they may contain up to 99 per cent of $CaCO_3$, various shades of grey, pink, buff, brown, and black. Unless they are intensely dolomitised they effervesce readily when tested with a drop of dilute hydrochloric acid owing to the evolution of carbon dioxide, CO_2:

$$CaCO_3 \; + \quad 2HCL \quad \rightarrow \; CaCl_2 \; + \; H_2O \; + \; CO_2$$

| Limestone | Hydrochloric | Calcium | Water | Carbon |
| (calcite) | acid | chloride | | dioxide |

Limestones are also very variable in texture; they may be composed of visible shell fragments (fossils), they may be fine-grained (microscopic fossils being visible only in a thin-section under the microscope), or highly crystalline when the original texture has been altered by the passage of ground-water, or by having been heated up in the Earth's crust. In the latter case the metamorphosed limestone is called marble.

Sandstone As its name indicates, a sandstone is a sand in which the grains have been cemented together by mineral matter derived from the soluble mineral matter carried in groundwater, which circulates through the rocks. Like limestones, sandstones are sedimentary rocks characterised by being bedded or stratified, and sometimes containing fossils which are the remnants of animals or plants living in, or carried into, the environment in which the sands were deposited.

There are many sandstones in the Peak District. Some are coarse and contain waterworn pebbles, when they can be called conglomeratic sandstones; some are composed of rather large angular grains of the common mineral quartz (of which most of the yellow sands on the sea-shores around Britain are composed), so that they have been called 'grits' or even 'gritstones', though this latter term is not one which should be encouraged. Others are so fine-grained that their detrital character can only just be discerned with a pocket-lens, and indeed there are a few which require examination in thin-section under a microscope in order to determine the nature of the grains.

The colours of sandstones are not as wide-ranging as those of limestones. They are usually grey, buff, pink or purplish-brown when fresh, but usually weather to a brown or dark greyish-brown colour. The colour of an unweathered sandstone depends primarily upon the nature of the minerals making up the grains, the extent to which any of these such as feldspars have decomposed, and the character of the mineral matter coating the grains or cementing them together.

Some sandstones split readily parallel to the bedding and have been used for farmhouse roofs in the Peak District; they are then described as 'flaggy'. Others have parting planes oblique to the bedding; this is known as cross- or false-bedding. If it can be shown to be due to the action of currents it is often designated current-bedding (Figure 4).

Sandstones can originate in a wide range of environments; some are formed on dry land as 'aeolian' or blown sand, others are deposited in the flood-plains of rivers, in lakes, estuaries, deltas, and in the sea. Marine sands form in the tidal zone, in shallow water and sometimes by the action of turbidity currents in deep water.

On the whole, sandstones are not very fossiliferous, and apart from fragmentary land plants, the sandstones of the Peak District are very poor in fossils.

Mudstone and shale Mudstone is a lithified mud, the fine mineral particles being cemented together by the decomposition products of some of the less stable minerals, or as in the case of sandstones, by mineral matter either siliceous or calcareous carried in solution in ground-water. Mudstone breaks into irregular pieces without any reference to the bedding or stratification planes.

Shale is a mudstone which is fissile or laminated, breaking into thin

Fig 4 Cross-bedding in sandstones (Rough Rock) at Stake Edge, near Errwood Reservoir, Goyt Valley, Cheshire

sheets or laminae parallel to the bedding planes. Fossils are sometimes the cause of lamination.

Mudstones and shales are usually grey or blue-grey in colour: they generally look darker when they are wet. They may form in many environments from lakes (lacustrine) to estuaries (estuarine) and in seas (marine). Many are deposited in habitats where organisms are abundant, and consequently both shales and mudstones may be very fossiliferous. The fine grain of these rocks allows for the preservation of many delicate organic details.

Mudstones and shales are common rocks in the Peak District, especially outside the predominantly limestone area. Most have originated in estuarine, deltaic, or marine environments.

Seat-earths occurring beneath coal seams are generally mudstones, containing fossil roots, and represent the substratum upon which the plants grew. As the plants during life removed the salts of sodium and postassium in particular, the resulting so-called 'fireclays' are not readily fusible and are, therefore, economically valuable as refractory materials. The plants of some coal seams grew upon sand rather than mud; the resulting hard flinty seat-earth, usually containing fossil roots, is called ganister.

Coal Although strictly speaking coal is a fossil fuel and not a rock, it may be considered here as a sedimentary rock since it occurs as a bedded or stratified deposit along with sandstone, mudstone and shale, and more rarely along with limestone. Coal originated from peat formed from dead plant material. A considerable amount of bacterial decomposition took place, but this was brought to an end by burial. Subsequently, owing to pressure from overlying sediments, compressive stress within the crust and increases in temperature, the original peat has undergone a process of devolatilisation involving the loss of hydrogen, nitrogen, oxygen, and sulphur and a corresponding relative increase in the carbon percentage.

Coals occur as beds or seams; they usually split parallel to the bedding along muddy partings or sometimes along surfaces covered with a dirty charcoal-like material, known as fusain, in which plant form is obvious, and which has been attributed to forest fires.

Coal is usually well jointed perpendicular to the bedding and usually in two directions, the most marked being known as the 'cleat'.

Thin coals occurring on the fringes of the Peak District have been worked in the past.

Dolerite A dark blue or blue-grey crystalline rock which occurs sporadically in the Peak District, cutting through the beds of limestone, and at the contact converting a small thickness of limestone into a marble-like rock. Dolerite is an igneous rock formed deep in the Earth's crust and ascending as a highly heated magma towards the surface. Sometimes the magma forces its way by hydrostatic pressure between beds of sedimentary rock to cool and crystallise as a tabular mass known as an igneous sill (Figure 5). Dolerite may also pierce the sedimentary rocks in the form of a pipe which could have led to the surface to give rise to a volcano, or along the more or less vertical fissures to form dykes (Figure 6).

It is necessary to examine a thin-section of a dolerite under the microscope to determine its texture and mineral composition. It will be found to consist of closely knit crystals of plagioclase feldspar and augite with, sometimes, the addition of the green mineral olivine. Some opaque minerals, iron ores such as magnetite, are generally

Fig 5   An igneous sill intruded into limestones; the dotted areas show the extent of contact metamorphism

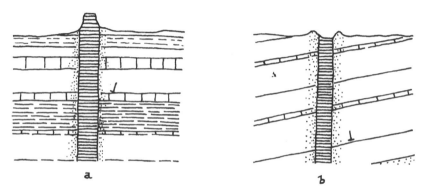

Fig 6   Igneous dykes. The dyke rock (a) is more resistant to weathering than the sediments into which it is intruded; the dyke rock (b) is less resistant. In both cases the extent of contact metamorphism is indicated by dots

present as dispersed grains and crystals.

Dolerite weathers by the chemical breakdown of the constituent minerals. Joint-blocks of the rock weather from all sides so that the weathered block looks rather like a large onion with layers peeling off by a process known as exfoliation. The weathered surface of dolerite is brown in colour.

Basalt   A dark blue or blue-grey finely crystalline rock. It is the most widespread type of lava forming in the world today, the dark highly-heated lava being poured out by some volcanoes of the central type (in which the feeder channel is a pipe) or from fissure volcanoes in which the magma wells up more or less vertical fissures and spreads out on the surface as lava flows. When the infilling of a fissure cools and consolidates it becomes a dyke.

Basalts may form on dry land or beneath the sea. In the latter case the rapid quenching causes the lava to form almost spherical masses closely connected with one another; this is a pillow lava. Gases contained in the lava and steam rising through the fluid lava as it comes to rest on a damp substratum give rise to voids or vesicles in the resulting rock. A basalt affected in this way would be termed a vesicular basalt. Should the vesicles later come to be filled with mineral matter, it would be called an amygdaloidal basalt.

In thin-section under the microscope a basalt is seen to consist of crystals of augite and lath-like crystals of plagioclase feldspar together with iron ores and sometimes olivine. Some glassy material may be present.

Basalt occurs as lava flows in the Peak District.

There are no representatives of the third major group of rocks, the metamorphic rocks, in the Peak District except for minor examples of thermal metamorphism such as where limestone in contact with an intrusive igneous rock has been rendered sugary in texture, or marmorised by recrystallisation to form a true marble.

MINERALS

Although all the rocks briefly described above are composed of minerals, it would not be possible to collect hand-specimens of minerals from them because the grains and crystals are so small. Fortunately, some of the rocks of the Peak District are cut by mineral veins. These are fissures in which a variety of minerals has crystallised out from warm or hot aqueous solutions ascending through the crust. Since some of these veins and other less regular mineral infillings include ores of lead, zinc, and copper, they have been exploited. The dumps of waste materials around the old mines have been combed for specimens by generations of students, but it is still possible to find good hand-specimens in some places especially if a little excavation of the mine waste is undertaken.

For the detailed determination of minerals, the reader is referred to

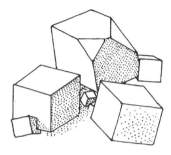

Fig 8   Fluorite: cubic crystals. The uppermost crystal shows two of the four directions of cleavage

an elementary text-book of mineralogy, such as *Rutley's Elements of Mineralogy* by H. H. Read.

The following notes on the more common minerals to be found in the Peak District are given so that mineral species can be identified in the field.

Calcite   The commonest form of calcium carbonate, $CaCO_3$. White or cream in colour, scratched readily with a pocket knife. Most characteristic feature is that the mineral breaks readily in three directions (cleavage) to give rhombohedral fragments. Calcite is found filling irregular spaces in some mineral veins and inside many fossils in limestone. When it crystallises freely calcite crystals are usually scalenohedra or as in 'nail-head' spar (Figure 7).

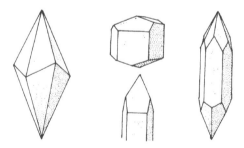

Fig 7   Calcite crystals: the scalenohedron is on the left, the commonly occurring 'nail-head' type is at the top in the middle

Fluorite Commonly known as fluor-spar, CaF_2. Variable in colour, pale yellow, pale blue, purple or colourless. A deep blue variety known as Blue John is found in the Peak District. Can be scratched with a pocket-knife. Crystallises as cubes; crystals may be elongated and packed together to give almost a fibrous appearance with colour bands perpendicular to the direction of elongation. The cleavage is octahedral so that when a cubic crystal is hit the corners split off (Figure 8).

Quartz A crystalline form of silica, SiO_2. Varies in colour, but usually white, pink or colourless. A purplish variety is amethyst. Can not be scratched with a pocket-knife, and scratches glass. This hardness test readily distinguishes it from purple varieties of fluorite. May crystallise as six-sided prisms terminated by six-sided pyramids (Figure 9), or may be massive. No cleavage; breaks like glass.

Galena An important ore of lead, lead sulphide PbS. Metallic lustre and lead coloured. Frequently crystallises as cubes with three directions of cleavage parallel to the cube faces. Sometimes massive but cleavage directions still evident. Some developments of galena in the Peak District carry an appreciable content of silver.

Fig 9 A group of quartz crystals. This is a natural size representation of a particular specimen but sizes are wide-ranging

Sphalerite Commonly call zinc blende, zinc sulphide ZnS. Waxy or resinous lustre and brownish colour. Crystals are combinations of crystal forms including the cube.

Barytes Commonly called 'heavy spar', barium sulphate $BaSO_4$. Its primary distinction from calcite or fluorite is due to its high specific gravity, so that a specimen of barytes feels much heavier than a specimen of calcite having the same volume. This character, however, does not distinguish it from all other minerals because others which are salts of barium or strontium such as celestite and strontianite also have a high specific gravity. Barytes, however, is the only one of these minerals which occurs commonly in the Peak District.

Barytes is variable in colour; it may be white, pale blue, pink, yellow, rarely colourless. May be scratched with a pocket-knife and is not affected by dilute hydrochloric acid. May develop well formed crystals or may be massive. Crystals often flattened (bladed habit) and terminations tending to occur in clusters.

Pyrite Iron pyrites or 'fool's gold' is iron sulphide, FeS_2. A very common mineral found as crystals or disseminations in all the rocks developed in the Peak District. Colour is brass yellow, lustre metallic. Crystals are generally cubes or pyritohedra. Decomposes by oxidation to produce a brown hydrated ferric oxide (frequently gelatinous) and free sulphuric acid; the latter may react with any calcareous material, such as limestone and calcareous fossils in shales, to produce calcium sulphate, gypsum, $CaSO_4.2H_2O$. The clear transparent crystal varieties of this are called selenite.

Chalcopyrite Copper pyrites, $CuFeS_2$. Occurs usually as small crystals, massive, or disseminations. Easily distinguished from pyrite by its deeper yellow almost golden colour.

Malachite A hydrated basic copper carbonate, $CuCO_3. Cu(OH)_2$. Easily recognised by its bright green colour. Usually occurs massive or stalagmitic with a smooth or botryoidal surface. Banding in various shades of green.

Azurite is another hydrated basic copper carbonate $2CuCO_3.Cu(OH)_2$. Characteristic deep azure colour. Usually massive or earthy.

Chert   A grey to black form of cryptocrystalline silica, rather like flint but breaks with a flat fracture as opposed to the conchoidal one in flint. Occurs as nodules and tabular masses in the upper parts of the Carboniferous Limestone of the Peak District. Chert is used in the pottery industry.

FOSSILS

The third group of materials available to the geologist, and frequently collected by amateurs who can do a signal service in this way, is the fossils. A fossil consists of the remains or traces of any animal or plant of the past preserved in the rocks. It is not the purpose of this book to enable the naming or determination of a fossil in other than a general way. The Peak District contains many rocks which are highly fossiliferous, and the beginner should refer to the excellent handbook on *British Palaeozoic Fossils* published by the British Museum (Natural History). More advanced work will require reference to the monographs of the Palaeontographical Society, Palaeontological Memoirs of the Geological Survey, Bulletins of the British Museum (Natural History) etc.

1   ANIMALS

Brachiopods: a very ancient group of invertebrates which have always been marine but which have now lost their former importance in marine faunas. Characterised by having two generally calcareous shells or valves hinged together by means of two teeth in the more convex valve and two sockets in the lesser convex or sometimes concave valve. The more convex (pedicle) valve often has a prominent beak or umbo which may be incurved. Beneath this beak in the same valve there may be a perforation, the pedicle foramen, through which a fleshy stalk passed to anchor the animal down to the substratum. In some

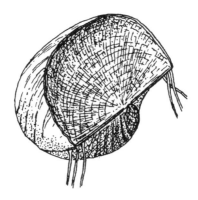

Fig 10   A brachiopod *Pugilis pugilis* from the Carboniferous Limestone (D$_2$ zone, Miller's Dale), showing probable position of growth and anchoring spines. Natural size

brachiopods this pedicle atrophied and the animal was anchored down by external calcareous spines (Figure 10). Sometimes the valves of fossil brachiopods have been disarticulated, and if the infilling rock or matrix is cleared away, impressions of the muscles by which the animal opened and closed its valves may be seen. The valves of a brachiopod are generally unequal in size but the plane of symmetry passes through both valves. This enables one to distinguish, at a glance, between brachiopods and bivalves (see below).

Some limestones in the Peak District are very rich in brachiopods which are extremely well preserved. Exceptionally the preservation is such as to retain traces of the original colour-banding on the external surfaces of the valves.

Bivalves: also known as lamellibranchs because of the general plate-like form of the gills in the living animals. A very ancient group of organisms which have adapted themselves to fresh-water as well as marine habitats. In addition to this adaptation there have been further ones, accompanied by anatomical changes, by which bivalves may be free to move about on the substratum, be fixed to it, or burrow into it.

A typical bivalve has two asymmetric but equal calcareous

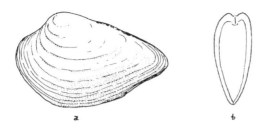

Fig 11 A bivalve: *Carbonicola pseudorobusta* Trueman from the Coal Measures. a, view of left valve showing growth lines; b, cross section. Two thirds natural size

valves (Figure 11) such that one is the mirror image of the other, so that the plane of symmetry passes between the valves. The valves may be articulated by means of a horny ligament along the hinge-line aided by teeth and sockets in both valves. Internal muscles are present for closing the valves, but opening is performed by the ligament which acts as a reversed C-spring. After death the internal muscles decay, the ligament operates and the articulated valves splay open. Both marine and non-marine bivalves occur in the rocks of the Peak District.

Goniatites: an ancient long-extinct group of marine molluscs characterised by having a spirally coiled shell divided internally into chambers by plates known as septa, the animal occupying the last-constructed and largest chamber. These animals were free-swimming organisms which lived in great numbers when some of the marine deposits of the Peak district were laid down. The shells were often thin and fragile so that they were compressed by sedimentation and later compaction. The junction between the edge of each septum and the surrounding shell was crimped in an angular fashion, from which the term *goniatite* was derived, and this junction, known as the septal suture, becomes visible when the outer layer of the shell is removed. The nature of the septal suture, which is constant for a given species, is one of the characters which has been found to be useful in the classification of goniatites (Figure 12).

Corals: various groups of organisms akin to the modern sea-

Fig 12   A goniatite *Goniatites crenistria* Phillips, stripped of most of the outer shell to show septal sutures and the infilled septal chambers or camerae. Natural size.

anemones have, for hundreds of millions of years, had the capacity of secreting calcium carbonate from sea-water to produce an external structure called a corallum. This consists of series of plates and other structures intimately related in their geometrical arrangement to the living tissues of the animal or animals responsible for their growth. A corallum may be *simple*, or *solitary* where it is secreted by a free-living organism in no way connected with its neighbours, or it may be *compound* or *colonial* (Figure 13), where the calcareous structure consists of numerous corallites, each corallite having been secreted by an animal in protoplasmic contact with its neighbours by a process of budding or asexual reproduction.

Modern reef-building marine corals require very special environmental conditions, notably warm mud-free sea-water not exceeding the depth to which sunlight can penetrate. There are numerous corals in some of the limestones of the Peak District, but as they are all extinct it can not be easily assumed that their presence denotes the same sort of environment as that favoured by modern corals.

Crinoids: these are animals which have a long geological history during which they have always been marine; they do not constitute important members of marine faunas today. Crinoids

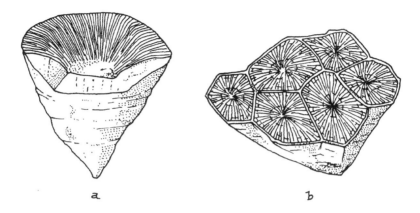

Fig 13 Rugose corals: a, simple; b, compound. One third natural size

are characterised by having a fivefold or pentameral symmetry, a symmetry which is commonplace in the plant kingdom, but which is unknown outside the phylum Echinodermata (to which starfish, sea-urchins or echinoids, and crinoids belong) in the animal kingdom. The modern crinoid *Antedon* is free-swimming, but most of the extinct crinoids have been sessile. Attached to the sea-floor by a long jointed calcareous 'stem', the animal is housed in a 'test' built of calcareous plates with mouth and anus, at the top of this stem, and is surrounded by five branching flexible 'arms' which collect food and direct it to the mouth (Figure 14).

Many limestones in the Peak District are *crinoidal.* consisting of sections of the stems, known as columnals or ossicles, and occasional plates. As the hard parts were articulated they readily broke up under the action of currents, and in the Peak District specimens with any degree of completeness are rare.

2 PLANTS

Plants have a long geological history in terrestrial, freshwater, and marine habitats.

Fossil plants which grew on land or in the sea are found, generally in a fragmentary state, in various rocks in the Peak District. Though all extinct, most of them are readily identified

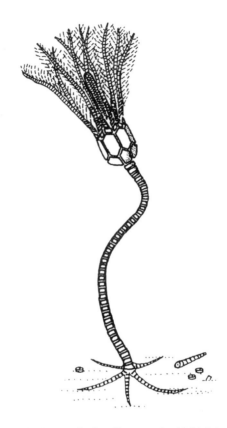

Fig 14 A typical sessile Lower Carboniferous crinoid. Height variable but some approaching one metre

as plants; they may be leaves, stems, and roots. A common plant stem in certain sandstones, shales, and mudstones in *Calamites* (Figure 15) which, largely because of the existence of prominent joints or nodes, readily reminds the finder of the modern marsh-loving horsetail, *Equisetum*. This plant had a hollow stem which, during and after burial, became filled with sandy or muddy sediment. The fossil *Calamites* resulting from this consists of an internal mould of the stem in sandstone or mudstone, bearing on its outside parallel vertical markings and impressions of the nodes. The former green plant-material may be represented by a

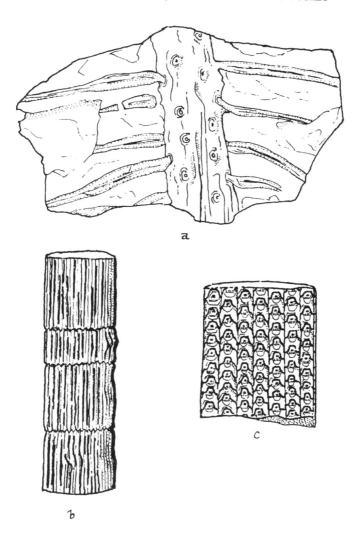

Fig 15   Common Upper Carboniferous plants. a, *Stigmaria* sp. roots in fireclay;
b, *Calamites* sp.; c, *Sigillaria* sp. Approximately one third natural size

thin film of coal on the outside of the mould.

A fossil plant of common occurrence in the seat-earths of coal
seams is the root *Stigmaria* (Figure 15)

FOSSILS AS TIME AND ENVIRONMENT INDICATORS.

Organisms have been evolving for over 3,000 million years so that fossils of those with hard parts can be used to relatively date the sedimentary rocks in which they occur. They also give evidence of the conditions under which they lived. For example, corals in the Carboniferous Limestone probably indicate tropical conditions. This is confirmed by palaeomagnetic studies which indicate a latitude of about 19°S when the limestone was deposited. At that time the Atlantic Ocean did not exist. The changes in position of land-masses are due to the movement of crustal plates in accordance with the theory of Plate Tectonics.'

CHAPTER 3

The Geological Time-Scale

For more than 4,500 million years the external processes of denudation and deposition have been in operation on the Earth, igneous activity and metamorphism have been at work deep in the crust, and volcanoes have been pouring their heated products on to the surface, and their hot dusts and gases into the atmosphere. The spatial distribution and relationships of these phenomena at any given time have been determined by processes operating beneath the crust in the Earth's mantle, that massive spherical shell between the crust and the core.

Life has existed for more than 3,000 million years on the Earth. Evidence is derived not only from the presence of fossils in many sedimentary rocks; from a variety of extremely ancient sediments organic residues have been extracted by chemical methods and some of their constituents have been identified with those commonly found in organisms today. Generally speaking, fossils consist of the resistant or hard parts of animals and plants, such as shells, bones and tough cuticles. It is common knowledge that bacterial decomposition and destruction by certain animals is a normal happening when an animal dies; the soft tissues quickly disappear, but the hard parts may survive if they are covered by accumulating sediment; this not only inhibits further physical damage and continued bacterial decomposition but provides a situation in which mineralising fluids may render hard parts very resistant. There are rare exceptions, where a fine-grained sediment retains a faithful impression of soft-bodied animals such as worms and jellyfish.

For the most part, the sporadic occurrences of fossils in some of the most ancient sediments on the Earth consist of impressions which indicate that many of the most ancient organisms were entirely soft-bodied.

It would appear that a remarkable physiological change affected many animals about 570 million years ago – the attainment of the ability to secrete salts, especially calcium carbonate, from sea-water to produce protective shells and structures offering support to some of the soft parts.

It is for this reason that many sediments deposited during the last 570 million years or so of the Earth's history contain abundant fossils, the remains or traces of animals and plants living in or carried into the environment of deposition. The study of these fossils affords the most reliable evidence as to whether this environment was a lake, a shallow sea, or a deep oceanic basin.

Towards the end of the eighteenth century, students of geology in Great Britain, France, Germany, and Italy recognised sedimentary rocks as pages of the Earth's history. It fell to William Smith, an English civil engineer and surveyor, to state the principles which must underlie the construction of a geological time scale. These are:

1   In any undisturbed succession of sediments the oldest bed is at the bottom and the youngest is at the top.
2   Each particular bed or stratum can be identified by the fossils which are included in it.
3   Extinction of an animal or plant species is permanent.

As far as the first principle is concerned any sequence of sediments which has not been overturned, as may happen in the case of some extreme folding, may be regarded as undisturbed.

In the Peak District, as in so many other areas, the sedimentary rocks are no longer in their original horizontal positions. They are now inclined, the angle between the bedding planes and the horizontal being called the angle of dip of the sediments. It follows that if we walk across country in the direction of dip of the rocks we pass from older to younger sediments.

On the basis of fossil faunas and floras, extinctions, and the appearance of new forms, the succession of sediments deposited during the last 570 million years or so, in Great Britain, has been divided into a number of 'systems' (see Appendix I). The time represented by each System of rocks is called a Period. In the Peak District we are concerned largely with rocks comprising the Carboniferous System; by studying them we can build up the history of the Carboniferous Period in that area. By applying William Smith's second principle we could compare the fossils from a particular group of beds in the Carboniferous system in the Peak District with those obtained from some part of the Carboniferous system in another near or distant area. If the fossils were found to be essentially the same, the two groups of beds could be equated or correlated and in this way episodes in the Carboniferous period could be recognised.

Periods have been grouped into Eras, also on a broad palaeontological basis, while Systems have been divided into stages and zones by the use of the more refined study of fossils.

Considering their small area, the British Isles are remarkable in having representatives of all the systems, and thereby concrete evidence of all the geological periods. The geological time-scale (Appendix I), which is purely relative, has been adopted internationally. The immense amount of geological time prior to the beginning of the Cambrian period can not be subdivided on the basis of included fossils, and for our purpose it can be referred to as the Precambrian.

Igneous rocks (those which have cooled from a state of fusion) associated with the sedimentary rocks can also be dated on this relative time-scale. The simplest case concerns the extrusive or volcanic rocks where, for example, a lava which flowed on to the top of accumulating sediments is, subsequent to cooling, covered by later sediments. It may produce slight metamorphic effects upon the sediments with which it is in contact, and waterworn fragments of lava may occur in the sediments immediately succeeding it. William Smith's first principle applies; the lava is younger than the sediments upon which it rests, and older than those which cover it. Provided that the sediments contain fossils, their relative age can be determined and the age of the volcanic episode follows. Several lava flows occur in the Carboniferous rocks of the Peak District and these conclusions can be verified in the field.

It is frequently not as easy to determine with any degree of precision the relative age of an intrusive igneous rock, one which has forced or melted its way into sediments below the surface. The intrusion must be later than the youngest sediment it alters or metamorphoses, and this will yield the maximum possible relative age. If a sediment can be found which rests upon an eroded surface of the intrusive igneous rock, or if pebbles of the igneous rock are included in the sediment, then the minimum possible relative age of the intrusion can be determined on the relative time-scale, provided that some of the sediments are fossiliferous.

It is very largely through the determination of the relative ages of igneous rocks that a radiometric time-scale, using the year as the unit, has been built up during the last sixty years. Certain chemical elements such as radium, uranium, thorium, rubidium and potassium have radioactive isotopes. They disintegrate, at rates which can be measured, and behave as natural clocks. The basic assumption is that disintegration began at the moment of crystallisation of the mineral containing a small amount of the radioactive element. For this reason, generally speaking, only igneous rocks can be used to build up such a timescale. This method also affords an invaluable opportunity for dating the Precambrian rocks which, owing to the paucity of fossils in any of their sediments, can not be subdivided satisfactorily on the relative geological time-scale.

As sedimentary rocks consist of detrital and precipitated soluble mineral material, derived perhaps second- or third-hand from the original igneous rock, radiometric methods for age-determination can not usually be applied to them. The most notable exception is that supplied by radio-carbon C^{14}, which is very restricted in its applications as a geological tool; it may be used for the direct age-determination of organic materials, such as wood and bone, up to a maximum age of about 50,000 years. In the Peak District this method has occasionally been used to date animal bones in cave-earths.

Geological Structure of the Peak District

Apart from some sporadic thin deposits of Pleistocene and Recent age, and some locally occurring sands, clays and gravels which are probably of Tertiary age, the rocks cropping out at the surface in the Peak District are all of Carboniferous age. From the Peak District proper, these rocks also form the hilly country to the west as far as the eastern edge of the Cheshire Plain which is formed of Triassic rocks. In the west, the junction between the Carboniferous and Triassic rocks is a fault. The fault is known as the Red Rock Fault; it has a considerable westerly downthrow, which means that on the west or downthrow side of the fault the Carboniferous rocks lie hidden beneath six hundred metres or more of Triassic rocks (Figure 16).

For our purposes, the southern boundary of the Peak District can be taken at about the latitude of Ashbourne where the Carboniferous rocks can be seen to disappear southwards beneath an increasing thickness of Triassic rocks underlying the Midland Plain. The junction here is an unconformable one; the reddish Triassic rocks rest upon an eroded surface of Carboniferous rocks in which the beds dip differently from those of the Trias.

Along the south-western edges of the Peak District there are several detached patches or outliers of Triassic rocks showing similar unconformable relationships to the underlying Carboniferous rocks; the more important of these outliers occur in the area around the River Churnet to the south of Leek in Staffordshire, and in the Rudyard Valley to the north of that town.

There are no rocks of Permian age exposed, and it is clear that at least in the areas immediately surrounding the Triassic inliers and in the belt of country along the southern margin of the Peak District the landscape is one which was developed during Permian-Triassic times. This old landscape has been exhumed by the denudation of the

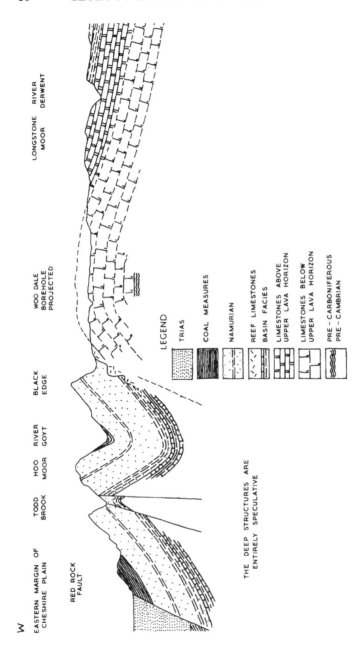

Fig 16   Diagrammatic section from the Cheshire Plain eastwards across the Peak District. The length of the section is about 40km and the vertical scale is exaggerated about ten times to portray the gross structure; consequently the angles of dip are much greater than on the ground

mantle of red Triassic rocks, and is now in process of modification. It could well be that the major features of the Peak District landscape were roughed out in Triassic times and have been undergoing modification since the mantle of Triassic and more recent deposits was removed.

The Carboniferous rocks of the Peak District are shown in Appendix III. The Lower Carboniferous rocks exposed at the surface are mainly limestones with several interbedded lava flows. All the limestones are marine and some of the lavas may have been erupted under water. The most common fossils in the limestones are brachiopods, corals, and crinoid fragments.

In 1905, Vaughan, on the basis of brachiopods and corals, divided the Carboniferous Limestone of the Avon Gorge into a number of faunal zones such as S(*Seminula*) and D(*Dibunophyllum*). These were subdivided e.g. D_1. This scheme had shortcomings when applied elsewhere but persisted until 1976 when a scheme of *Stages* based upon palaeontology and cycles of deposition was introduced. Vaughan's scheme is retained here only because it appears so frequently in the literature for 70 years. A rough correlation of the two schemes is shown in Appendix II.

The Upper Carboniferous rocks of the Peak District comprise a thick lower group of shales and sandstones known as the Namurian or Millstone Grit, and an upper group of shales, sandstones, and thin coal seams belonging to the Lower Westphalian or Lower Coal Measures. The major part of the Coal Measures has been removed by denudation mainly in Permo-Trias times. The total thickness of Carboniferous rocks exposed in the Peak District is in the order of 2,000m.

The general disposition of the outcrops of the three major subdivisions of the Carboniferous rocks is shown in the sketch-map, Figure 17.

As seen in a W–E section (Figure 18) the Carboniferous rocks between the Red Rock Fault and the Derbyshire coalfield are folded into a low anticlinorium, that is a broad anticline with minor folds along its limbs. Both the broad structure and the subsidiary folds are obvious in the field.

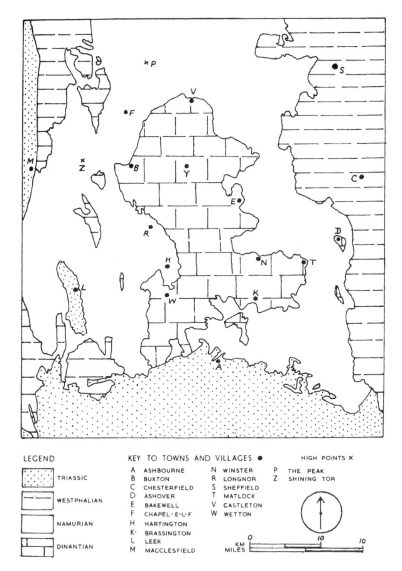

LEGEND

▦	TRIASSIC
▤	WESTPHALIAN
▢	NAMURIAN
▧	DINANTIAN

KEY TO TOWNS AND VILLAGES ●

A	ASHBOURNE	N	WINSTER
B	BUXTON	R	LONGNOR
C	CHESTERFIELD	S	SHEFFIELD
D	ASHOVER	T	MATLOCK
E	BAKEWELL	V	CASTLETON
F	CHAPEL-E-L-F	W	WETTON
H	HARTINGTON		
K·	BRASSINGTON		
L	LEEK		
M	MACCLESFIELD		

HIGH POINTS ×

P   THE PEAK
Z   SHINING TOR

KM
MILES

0   10   10

Fig 17   Geological sketch map showing the main divisions of rocks in the Peak District and the area immediately around it. *Crown Copyright. Based on maps of the Geological Survey of Great Britain, and reproduced by permission of the Controller, Her Majesty's Stationery Office*

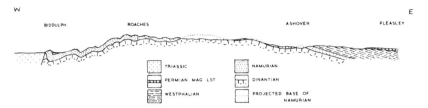

Fig 18 Sketch-section across the southern Pennines to show the general structure. Length of section about 20km. Vertical scale greatly exaggerated

As a result of the denudation of this broad anticlinal structure, the oldest Carboniferous rocks, the Carboniferous Limestone, form the core and crop out in the limestone uplands cut by valleys or dales, frequently dry, which is commonly regarded as the Peak District. The base of the Carboniferous is nowhere exposed. If the unexposed part of the Lower Carboniferous succession proved in the Geological Survey borehole is taken into account, then the total thickness of Carboniferous rocks in the Peak District is about 3,100m.

Surrounding the limestone terrain on the west, north, and east is the entirely different kind of country, largely peat-covered hills or moors carved out of the Namurian rocks. In the south, the red Triassic rocks rest directly and unconformably upon the limestone, clear evidence that the broad anticlinal structure in the Carboniferous rocks existed in Triassic times.

The subsidiary folds superimposed upon the main anticlinal structure are present in the west and central areas; their axes run roughly N–S, and in the moorland country to the west of Buxton this gives rise to striking escarpments or 'edges' formed by the sandstones of the Namurian running in this direction (Figure 19).

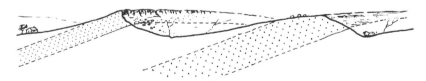

Fig 19 Namurian sandstone escarpments and dip-slopes showing the relationship between surface and structure

When the inclinations or dips of the limestones are examined in detail it is seen that the main anticline is rather flat-topped with minor ripples on its surface, and that the only appreciable dips are to be seen where the limestones disappear beneath the overlying Namurian rocks. This also occurs around the northern fringe of the limestone terrain from Barmoor Clough to Castleton. In fact, northwards from Buxton to Barmoor Clough the limestones dip to the west; from Barmoor Clough to Castleton the limestones dip northwards beneath the Namurian country including Kinder Scout, and from Castleton

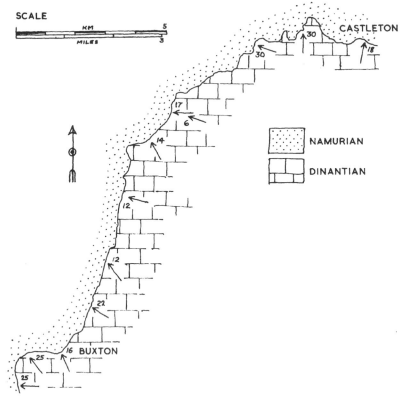

Fig 20 Sketch-map of the Namurian-Dinantian boundary between Castleton and Buxton to show the change in the direction of dip of the limestones along the junction. The amount of dip increases towards the boundary

to Bakewell the dip of the limestones gradually swings round to the east. It is for this reason that the structure of the limestone area has been referred to as a dome (Figure 20).

The Carboniferous rocks of the Peak District are affected by numerous faults, some of the more powerful ones running E–W and others N–S. In the limestone area some faults have served as routes for the passage of rising mineralising solutions, and vertical fissures giving no evidence of relative displacement of the two sides have acted in the same way so that they are marked by mineral veins or lodes. Calcite, fluorite, barytes, galena, and sphalerite are the most commonly occurring minerals. Many lodes or rakes show horizontal striations or 'slickensides' on their limestone walls, indicating that the last phase of movement was horizontal as in a tear- or wrench-fault. Outside the limestone area, mineral veins are almost unknown; there are a few veins of barytes in the Namurian rocks, and sporadic occurrences of galena in the Coal Measures are recorded from time to time.

As well as including volcanic rocks, such as lavas and tuff bands, the limestones of the Peak District are affected by some igneous intrusions, notably dolerite sills and pipes; igneous dykes are very rare, and those that have been described, as at Buxton Bridge in Great Rocks Dale near Buxton, are now poorly exposed.

CHAPTER 5

The Valley of the River Wye:
Buxton to Little Longstone

The Derbyshire River Wye has it headwaters in peaty streams in the high moorland Millstone Grit country to the west of Buxton, although the official source of the river is at Wye Head in Macclesfield Road, Buxton. Here on the north side of the road a stream can be seen to issue from limestone, the eroded top of which is succeeded unconformably by blue shales of Namurian age.

From here the Wye proceeds in a general easterly direction from Buxton to Little Longstone, a distance of nearly twenty kilometres cutting right across the major anticlinal structure affecting the Carboniferous Limestone, incising itself and its tributaries into the limestones and associated volcanic rocks. From Little Longstone the river is deflected in a south-easterly direction through Ashford-in-the-Water and Bakewell until after about another ten kilometres it joins the River Derwent at Great Rowsley, and so takes water from the western side of the Pennines into the North Sea.

The town of Buxton is situated at an altitude of more than 300m

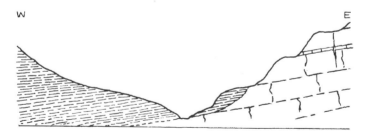

Fig 21 Section across the Nun Brook north of Buxton to show the unconformable relationship between Dinantian limestones (brickwork pattern) and the Namurian shales and mudstones (hatched)

46

above sea-level. It was formerly renowned as a spa for the treatment of rheumatic diseases, and its thermal waters which issue at a constant temperature of 38°C were recognised as beneficial by the Romans. The lower part of the town is built on Namurian shales; these were well exposed some years ago when a trench for a new sewer was excavated along Spring Gardens, the main street. The higher part of the town is founded on the Carboniferous Limestone (Figure 21), and indeed limestones with fossils, which indicate an horizon a little higher than the Upper Lava of Miller's Dale, may be seen at Holker Road just south of Spring Gardens. Here we have the Namurian occurring at a lower altitude than the Carboniferous Limestone not on account of the direction and amount of dip, but because the Namurian shales were deposited on an eroded surface of the limestone. The junction is an uncomfortable one. Moreover, several scores of metres of limestone had been removed by denudation in the Buxton area prior to the deposition of Namurian shales. This will be seen to be in marked contrast with the situation on the eastern limb of the main anticline.

The valley of the River Wye changes it name several times. The portion nearest to Buxton is Ashwood Dale; it begins at the eastern end of Spring Gardens, Buxton, as a funnel-shaped entrance into a limestone-sided valley floored with Namurian shales. The latter quickly die out eastwards. At the supermarket roughly a kilometre south-east of the railway viaduct in Spring Gardens the well bedded limestones are visible, in the old railway cutting, dipping westwards at a low angle. Interbedded with them is a brown-weathering rock which upon closer examination is seen to be a vesicular basaltic lava. Fossils found in the limestones about ten metres below the base of this lava, and especially those in a rich fossiliferous band with the brachiopod *Davidsonina septosa* (Figure 22) shows that this is the Lower Lava of Miller's Dale. Consequently, the limestones in the cliffs between the gas works and Spring Gardens are the Miller's Dale Beds (Appendix IV).

As we walk down the valley in an easterly direction we are moving in a direction contrary to the dip of the rocks and consequently are moving into progressively lower beds; we say we are moving to lower

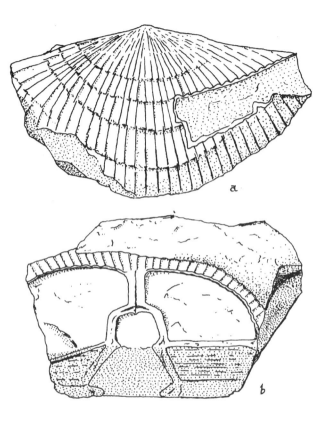

Fig 22 *Davidsonina septosa*. a, pedicle valve; b, weathered specimen of pedicle valve showing spondylium, teeth, etc. Natural size

horizons. This is an application of William Smith's first principle (p 35).

Between the supermarket and the Devonshire Arms in Ashwood Dale, the valley is defined by vertical mural cliffs in the thickly bedded Chee Tor Beds which lie beneath the Lower Lava. These Chee Tor limestones were named from a particularly fine exposure with that name in Chee Dale lower down the Wye Valley. They are generally thickly bedded and consist of fine detrital shell and crinoid material which has probably been winnowed by current action in a shallow-water environment. These limestones, over 100m in thickness, are

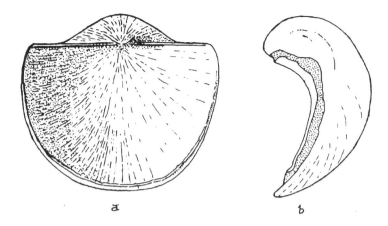

Fig 23 *Daviesiella llangollensis* (Davidson) from the Woo Dale Beds, S_2 zone.
a, brachial valve and umbo of pedicle valve; b, longitudinal section showing thick
pedicle valve on right, thinner brachial valve on left. Half natural size

generally very pure, analyses sometimes showing more than 99 per
cent of calcium carbonate. They have been much sought after and
worked in the Buxton area for the production of lime, ground
limestone for agricultural purposes, and limestone required on a large
scale for the chemical industry. Immense tonnages of these limestones have been removed especially in Great Rocks Dale, around
Peak Dale and Tunstead, at Grin Low to the south of Buxton, and
around Harpur Hill. Before 1945, the quarrying of limestone in this
part of the Peak District employed large numbers of men, but the
quarrying is now largely mechanised.

The calcining or 'burning' of limestone is a very ancient practice in
the Peak District, and hillocks of waste or relics of old limekilns can
be found on most hills where purer limestones crop out.

In the railway cutting above the Devonshire Arms in Ashwood
Dale the base of the Chee Tor Beds can be seen. Below these almost
white limestones are much darker limestones with the large thick-
shelled brachiopod *Daviesiella llangollensis* (Davidson), Figure 23,
along with some extremely fine-grained limestones called calcite
mudstones, chinastones, or calcilutites. These two sets of beds define

Fig 24   Fault plane exposed in Ashwood Dale Works Quarry, near Cunning Dale, Buxton. On left or downthrow side of fault are thickly bedded Chee Tor limestones; on right thinner bedded Woo Dale Beds

the junction between the $^*S_2$ and $^*D_1$ zones. The lower generally darker-coloured rocks may be referred to as the Woo Dale Beds; they are exposed intermittently down the valley as far as Woo Dale where the axis of the main anticline is crossed, and beyond to Topley Pike and Blackwell Mill. They are much more thinly bedded than the Chee Tor limestones, and beneath the calcite mudstone horizon tend to be extensively dolomitised. The Woo Dale Beds can be examined in some of the tributary dry valleys such as Cunning Dale, Kid Tor Dale, Woo Dale, and Deep Dale which enters the main valley at Topley Pike.

This part of the valley of the River Wye more or less follows the course of a fault which can be traced for several kilometres in an E–W direction. A superb exposure of this fault is to be found in the quarry to the north of the railway cutting high above the Devonshire Arms. It is a normal fault showing a 'hade' of about 30°, with slickensides on the fault plane and some calcite mineralisation. Dark limestones of the Woo Dale Beds appear on the north or upthrow side of the fault,

---

* Holkerian and Asbian stages, See Appendix I

and the almost white limestones of the Chee Tor Beds on the south or downthrow side (Figure 24).

The gentle westerly dip continues downstream as far as the confluence with the dry valley of Woo Dale which comes in from the north. Here on the north bank of the Wye the outcrops of thin limestones in the Woo Dale Beds clearly demonstrate the crossing of the main anticlinal axis, for to the east of Woo Dale a gentle easterly dip sets in. This change in the direction of dip can be observed by following the river for about 150m to the east and west of Woo Dale; at the confluence of the two dales crinoidal limestones in the Woo Dale Beds can be seen to be virtually horizontal and thus to mark the position of the fold axis in this area. The total thickness of Woo Dale Beds exposed in this Wye Valley section is just over 100m, and the oldest beds (or the lowest horizons) of the Carboniferous Limestone in north Derbyshire are exposed at the southern end of Woo Dale. Folds subsidiary to the main structure are responsible for the Woo Dale Beds being exposed at Peak Forest to the north of the Wye and at Duchess Cliff near Harpur Hill to the south, but the horizons attained are not quite as low as in Woo Dale.

THE CARBONIFEROUS BASEMENT

The nature, thickness, and zonal age of older Lower Carboniferous rocks lying beneath north Derbyshire is an intriguing problem, as is the age of the pre-Carboniferous rocks upon which they were deposited. Nowhere in the Peak District is the base of the Carboniferous exposed, a very different state of affairs from that in some other Carboniferous Limestone areas such as Bristol, Anglesey, North Wales, the Lake District and the northern Pennines. In the Avon Gorge at Bristol the Carboniferous Limestone is seen to succeed the Old Red Sandstone (Devonian) without any discordance, but in Anglesey the Carboniferous Limestone probably as low as the S_2 zone is seen to rest with spectacular unconformity upon Precambrian, Ordovician, and Silurian rocks. In Anglesey we can actually locate the Lower Carboniferous shoreline in various places, and all the evidence points to an ancient land-mass lying to the south of Anglesey. The northern shorelines of this land-mass, at various stages during the Lower Carboniferous, probably passed through what is now the Peak District.

Whether this is so can only be ascertained by putting down boreholes and examining the cores of rock produced for fossil or other evidence which may provide clues as to age.

One such borehole was put down by Imperial Chemical Industries Ltd in north Derbyshire in 1948 in an attempt to answer some of the questions. On purely theoretical grounds one could have argued that the Lower Carboniferous succession would be an incomplete one, with probably no representative of that part of Lower Carboniferous time known as the Tournaisian, but the rocks that composed the land mass inundated by the succeeding Viséan seas could be of almost any pre-Carboniferous age, from Precambrian to Silurian, and even some Old Red Sandstone (Devonian) was not beyond the bounds of possibility. For this borehole, the author selected a site on the crest of the main anticline at the confluence of Woo Dale with Wye Dale; the spot is now marked by a hut housing pumping-gear, for the borehole produces a plentiful supply of water.

The borehole passed through extensively dolomitised limestones to a depth of 272m when it passed into a breccia, a rock made up of angular and sub-rounded fragments of volcanic rocks. The cores yielded some macro-fossils; they and micro-fossils were sufficient to establish that all the limestones are of Viséan age and that no Tournaisian rocks are present; proof that this part of the Peak District was dry land during the whole of Tournaisian time about 345 million years ago.

Below two metres of breccia, the borehole penetrated highly inclined volcanic rocks, both lavas and ashes; the breccia appears to represent the weathered top of this volcanic terrain before it was inundated by the sea. The precise age of the volcanic rocks has not yet been determined. That they are of pre-Carboniferous age seems highly probable for they had undergone folding or tilting before the earliest of the Carboniferous limestones were deposited.

All the limestones seen so far in the Wye Valley section are of marine shallow-water origin; this is particularly true of the Chee Tor limestones which, in the extensive quarries in Great Rocks Dale, to the north of Topley Pike, show a good deal of contemporaneous potholing at several horizons. The beds are all very gently folded. All this points to deposition in shallow water on a slowly subsiding basement which acted as a rigid mass in the folding that followed the deposition of the Carboniferous rocks.

THE SEQUENCE EAST OF WOO DALE

To the east of Woo Dale the sequence of limestones encountered in descending order from Buxton is repeated in the reverse order. The dolomitised limestones and calcite mudstones are particularly well exposed in the cuttings along the former railway, in the roadside exposures beneath Topley Pike, and in the two dry valleys, Deep Dale on the south and Great Rocks Dale in the north. These limestones yield *Daviesiella llangollensis* and *Davidsonina carbonaria*, Figure 25, brachiopods indicating the Holkerian Stage, including the former S_2 zone.

Deep Dale, which joins Wye Dale at Topley Pike, is a typical Derbyshire dale, a deep, winding, dry valley with limestone cliffs along the top and scree slopes below. Deep Dale is formed from two tributary dales, Back Dale and Horseshoe Dale, which originate near Brierlow Bar about three kilometres south-south-west of Topley Pike.

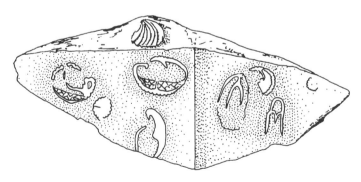

Fig 25 Block of S_2 limestone with the typical brachiopod *Davidsonina carbonaria* to show characteristic sections. The block is upside down (notice infilling of two brachiopods). Half natural size

It is a still quiet valley frequented by foxes, and in its northern reaches has a diminutive stream during the wetter months of the year. It was formerly popular to ascribe such dry valleys and limestone gorges to the collapse of caverns formed by the underground solution of limestone. Had this been the case it might be thought rather extraordinary that no gorge or dry valley is known which could have been produced by very recent collapse: such would surely be marked by chaotic fallen blocks. Deep Dale has all the appearance of having been eroded by a stream. The altitude of the River Wye at Topley Pike is 260m above sea-level, and this must be the level of the water-table or top of the zone of permanent saturation in these well jointed and soluble limestones. The small stream in Deep Dale rises at an altitude of about 285m above sea-level. To the south of the source of the stream the bed of the dale rises to almost 330m above sea-level; this is too high above the water-table for a stream to be sustained. Rainwater in these high reaches finds its way down joints in the limestones to join the main body of ground-water probably forty metres below the surface. It is quite impossible for this dry valley to have been eroded while the water-table was at its present level. The valley can only have been eroded when the water-table was at a higher level than the present. The fall in level of the water-table to its present position could have been brought about by a regional uplift after this and other dry valleys were eroded. There are two caves halfway up the valley side a little to the north of the source of the present stream and these must have been formed by solution below the level of the water-table. During the last century bones of Pleistocene mammals were found in one of these caves, so that it should be possible to deduce a minimum age for the regional uplift.

At the north end of Deep Dale at the foot of Topley Pike we get another exposure of the E–W fault which was seen higher up the Wye to the north of the Devonshire Arms. On the north or upthrow side of the fault we can see the dark-coloured limestones and calcite mudstones of the Woo Dale Beds, whilst high up on the south or downthrow side of the southerly-hading fault are the thickly bedded white Chee Tor limestones culminating in the summit of Topley Pike. The fault plane is easily accessible for close examination; there is considerable calcite mineralisation.

In the country to the south of Topley Pike, as far as the village of Chelmorton, there is a wide outcrop of the Chee Tor limestones. Many of the fields in this area contain remains of old limekilns. They are more than a hundred years old and were used for calcining lime from the high calcium carbonate Chee Tor limestones before these had been exploited on a large scale. Much of the coal needed for firing the kilns was brought from the Goyt's Moss coalfield in the Goyt Syncline to the west of Buxton (p 80). With the availability of mass-produced lime and ground limestone these small kilns have long since ceased to be used, and it is not easy to find one in a good state of preservation in the Peak District.

From Woo Dale eastwards to the great southward bend of the Wye at Little Longstone the beds dip generally eastwards on the eastern limb of the main anticline, though there are gentle anticlinal and synclinal flexures which locally reverse the gentle easterly dip. This traverse provides a fairly complete standard section of the Carboniferous Limestone for the Peak District. The natural sections in the dale sides are supplemented by fairly continuous exposures in the cuttings of the former main-line railway, and by several quarries and roadside exposures. The section suggests a conformable passage from the Carboniferous Limestone into the succeeding Millstone Grit or Namurian, a very different state of affairs from that on the western limb of the anticline where, as we have already seen, the Namurian rests with strong unconformity upon the Carboniferous Limestone in the vicinity of Buxton.

The Woo Dale limestones can be examined in the roadside exposure below Topley Pike and on the hillside to the north of the Wye; they are easily traced eastwards to Great Rocks Dale where their outcrop runs for some distance up this dale, and where at the southern end of the immense Tunstead quarries their dark dolomitised limestones and splintery white-weathering calcite mudstones are seen to pass beneath the almost white Chee Tor limestones.

In the Tunstead quarries the Chee Tor limestones belonging to the D_1 zone are about 125m thick; they are very thickly bedded or massive, beds often showing thicknesses of ten metres. These limestones are consistently pure with the calcium carbonate content sometimes exceeding 99 per cent; these are the limestones from which 'best Buxton lime' has been produced for many years. The typical limestone consists of finely comminuted brachiopod and crinoid debris, suggesting long-continued current action. Unbroken brachiopod shells are rare and corals are very infrequent. In their upper part these beds include a number of thin interbedded blue, sometimes pyritous, clay bands. Each band rests upon an eroded sometimes deeply potholed limestone surface, and appears to represent a volcanic ash. The potholed limestone surfaces could indicate uplift of the bed of the shallow sea, and the ash or tuff bands give evidence of volcanic activity spasmodically over a considerable period of time.

This volcanic activity culminated in the outpouring of the basaltic Lower Lava of which we have already seen a thin representative on the western limb of the anticline near Buxton. The Lower Lava is well developed in Great Rocks Dale. It and the associated Chee Tor limestones are affected by several E–W faults which have been encountered in the long quarry running on the western side of the dale almost from Buxton Bridge, south of Peak Dale, to the valley of the Wye. Near the northern end of this quarry the Lower Lava is in contact with the large intrusive mass of olivine dolerite at Water-swallows. From time to time it has been thought that the Water-swallows dolerite, which has been worked extensively as a roadstone under the name of 'Derbyshire Granite', could be a vent from which the Lower Lava emanated. There is now evidence that this intrusion is a sill of post-Carboniferous Limestone age.

The source of the Lower Lava has yet to be identified. The author is of the opinion that one feeder centre was situated in Great Rocks Dale about 500m south of Buxton Bridge. Unfortunately, much of the evidence has been quarried away, but over the past fifty years there have been temporary exposures of a dyke complex with extensive marmorisation of the surrounding limestones. Close to the dyke complex the lava flow is underlain by a thickness in excess of eight metres of intensely marmorised limestone, practically a true marble. The normal thermal metamorphic effect of the lava on the underlying limestones is negligible, a mere couple of centimetres or so of alteration.

In the main section, the Chee Tor limestones are again well exposed downstream from the Great Rocks Dale junction, in the beautiful mural cliffs which extend eastwards and northwards round the immense bend of the Wye which includes Chee Tor, the type locality. The very thick beds are cut by well developed vertical master-joints which determine the form of the cliffs. This section of the Wye Valley, from Topley Pike past Chee Tor to Miller's Dale, is probably the most grandiose and certainly the least frequented in the whole length of the river. Many of the exposures are difficult of access, but those close to the portals of the disused railway tunnels show the more important characteristics of these limestones.

To the north of the impressive bastion of Chee Tor, where the River Wye resumes its normal easterly direction of flow, the low regional dip has brought the top of the Chee Tor Limestones down to within fifty metres of river-level. The overlying Lower Lava is exposed alongside the footpath from Wormhill Springs at the confluence of Flag Dale with Chee Dale to the village of Wormhill but its outcrop is not visible within the main valley probably owing to faulting. The Lower Lava at Wormhill gives rise to a perched water-table and a spring from this has excavated the steep gully which joins Flag Dale near Wormhill Springs. The lava is an impervious rock preventing the further downward percolation of ground-water in the Miller's Dale Limestones which lie above the lava.

The beds succeeding the Lower Lava, the Miller's Dale Limestones, are well seen in the large disused quarry, called Station Quarry owing to its proximity to the former Miller's Dale railway station, on the north side of the Wye east of Wormhill Springs.

They comprise a thickness of about forty metres of thickly bedded light grey and sometimes almost white detrital limestones. Fossils are more common in the Miller's Dale Limestones than in the Chee Tor Limestones; they include brachiopods, especially species of *Productus* such as *Productus maximus*, colonial corals such as *Lithostrotion junceum* and *L. irregulare*, and simple corals, especially *Palaeosmilia*

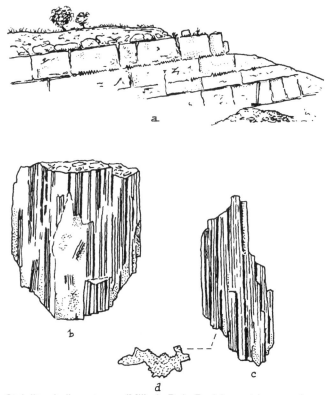

Fig 26   Stylolites in limestones (Miller's Dale Beds). a, old quarry face showing stylolites along bedding planes; b and c, hand specimens of stylolited junctions; d, cross-section of c. Half natural size

murchisoni (Edwards and Haime). These place the Miller's Dale Limestones in the [†]D$_1$ zone. Though by no means peculiar to these limestones, stylolites are well developed here. Stylolites are developed along bedding planes and appear in vertical section as zig-zag junctions between beds. They are due to one bed being pressed into another concomitant with solution, a case of pressure-solution (Figure 26).

---

* Brigantian Stage
† Asbian Stage

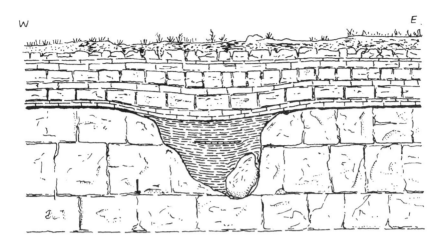

W   E

Fig 27   Idealised sketch of exposure in Miller's Dale Station yard (abandoned), showing channel cut in Miller's Dale Beds. The section is now largely overgrown with willows

The top of the Miller's Dale Limestones is well seen in Station Quarry, in an old quarry on the south side of the old railway track about 600m east of the railway viaduct, and in the old Miller's Dale Station yard. It is a prominently marked bedding plane which can be traced easily because the beds immediately above it are much darker in colour and contain occasional fossils indicating the *D_2 zone. In other words, the top of the Miller's Dale Beds is taken as the upper limit of the †D_1 zone.

The thinly bedded dark-coloured limestones called the Station Quarry Beds contain occasional nodules of chert, a crypto-crystalline variety of silica similar in some respects to flint. The base of these limestones is always sharp and sometimes highly irregular; for example, in the old Miller's Dale Station yard the topmost beds of the Miller's Dale Limestones were channelled by water-action prior to the deposition of the Station Quarry Beds, suggesting regional uplift at this time. In this particular exposure the base of the Station

---

* Brigantian Stage
† Asbian Stage

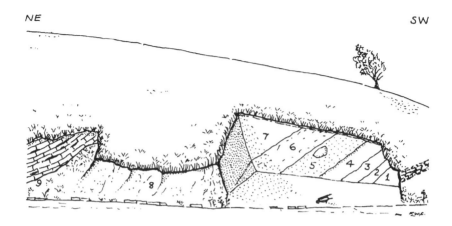

NE   *SW*

Fig 28   Temporary section at head of Taddington Dale in 1933 showing flow-units in Upper Lava which is dying out at this point. 1, amygdaloidal basalt; 2, brown spheroidally weathered basalt; 3, ochre-coloured basalt; 4, brown weathered basalt; 5, weathered basalt with included block; 6, weathered basalt; 7, hard blue amygdaloidal basalt; 8, weathered basalt; 9, thinly bedded dark limestones with chert

Quarry Beds sags over the channel which is largely filled with a blue shale with fish remains and a large limestone boulder (Figure 27).

Succeeding the Station Quarry Beds which are about eight metres thick in the quarry of that name is another basaltic lava called the Upper Lava. Its basal part forms the top of the face at the eastern end of Station Quarry. It is a brown-weathering amygdaloidal lava of basaltic composition. Its outcrop extends north of the quarry into the peculiar eminence known as Knot Low, and hereabouts the thickness of this Upper Lava is at least forty metres. Distinct flow units have been clearly recognised in the Upper Lava near Taddington to the south of Miller's Dale (Figure 28), so the lava must be regarded as comprising several outpourings piled one above the other, but probably of varying extent. The centre or centres of the eruptions which produced these flows are unknown; they probably lie close to Miller's Dale for this is the area of maximum thickness. The eruptions were probably submarine, and the earliest lava flow was preceded in some areas by a thin fall of ash.

The top of the Upper Lava is visible in the lower part of the large abandoned quarry to the south of the River Wye roughly opposite St Anne's Church in Miller's Dale. It is irregular and appears to be eroded. The lava is succeeded in this quarry by almost forty metres of thickly bedded pale-grey limestones, the Priestcliffe Limestones, which are poorly fossiliferous. At various horizons these limestones contain authigenic crystals of quartz most of them of microscopic dimensions, but many visible to the naked eye when the rock is broken. Possibly the presence of these six-sided prisms with pyramidal terminations are responsible for the name 'Diamond Hill' which lies to the west of the quarry. These small quartz crystals grew as independent crystallographic units within the limestone shortly after deposition.

The Priestcliffe Beds are surmounted at the top of the hill above the quarry by more than twenty metres of well bedded dark-grey limestones with nodular chert which contain some well preserved fossils. These are D_2 zone fossils including *Pugilis pugilis*, a productid, with a long trail (anteriorly extended valves) and spines, and the coral *Aulophyllum fungites*. The fossils are scattered as though they were moved from their living positions by currents.

Miller's Dale is that section of the valley of the Wye between Wormhill Springs and Litton Mill. The Buxton–Sheffield road crosses the river to the west of the hamlet of Miller's Dale and climbs high above the river on the north side. The river is followed by a road from St Anne's Church to Litton Mill and this access makes part of the valley popular for visitors. Since the closing of the main-line railway it has become quiet and offers a good centre for studying the geology in some detail.

Between the Angler's Rest hotel, near the confluence of Monk's Dale with the main valley, and the striking cliff of Raven's Tor, a subsidiary doming of the beds brings the Lower Lava, which had disappeared beneath Miller's Dale Limestones immediately east of Wormhill Springs, to the surface again. It can be examined along the roadside from the easternmost house in the hamlet, close to which it gives rise to a spring, eastwards as far as Raven's Tor where there is a splendid exposure of the top of the Lower Lava. The lava is highly vesicular, sometimes amygdaloidal, and is generally rather weathered. At Raven's Tor it has yielded blocks of limestone caught up in the lava containing fossil nautiloids unknown anywhere *in situ*. On account of the subsidiary doming the lava forms a lenticular outcrop over which the river flows.

The Miller's Dale Limestones form cliffs above the lava both north and south of the river. At Raven's Tor a low cave has developed at the limestone-lava junction, and the upper surface of the lava was very irregular when limestone sedimentation began again.

The Upper Lava crops out on the south side of the river above the old railway track, across the hillside known as Priestcliffe Lees. Exposures are rare and the outcrop is marked by lava fragments in the soil. It more or less coincides with the belt of trees, mainly hawthorn with some guelder rose; the latter grows much more frequently on lava than on limestone. This lava appears to have a constant thickness of about thirty-three metres. A detached circular outcrop of the Upper Lava occurs at Monksdale Cottages to the north of St Anne's Church, and here the outlier is capped with a few metres of the Priestcliffe Limestones.

Eastward from Raven's Tor the Miller's Dale Limestones continue at and above river-level for about two kilometres almost to the confluence of Cressbrook Dale. From opposite Tongue End it forms cliffs on the south side of the river and through that part of the valley known as Water-cum-Jolly Dale. Here the Wye follows a beautiful curved course and has all the appearance of having been incised as a result of regional uplift.

The behaviour of the Upper Lava is interesting and instructive to the east of Tongue End on Hammerton Hill, and to the south of Tongue End on the old railway line. It is better to examine the railway cutting first and to interpret Hammerton Hill in the light of this. The south face of the cutting is as in Figure 29. The inclined lava-limestone junction was regarded years ago as a faulted one; the beds on the east or downthrow side of the supposed fault were thought to be the dark limestones with chert above the Priestcliffe Beds at Miller's Dale Lime Works. Howeve there is no fault in the river cliffs beneath the railway cutting, the Miller's Dale Limestones being

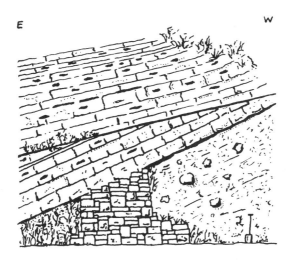

Fig 29 Section on south side of former railway track near Litton Mill showing the Miller's Dale Upper Lava dying out eastwards. The lava exposed to the west of the retaining wall contains angular and sub-rounded blocks of lava. Scale indicated by spade

continuous. Detailed investigation showed that the Upper Lava in the cutting is on the point of dying out eastwards. The lava itself contains loose blocks, and some of the irregularly thinly bedded limestones with chert above the lava contain waterworn fragments of lava near the contact. We have here then an example of the steep submarine front of a basaltic flow.

About thirty metres above this exposure, on the steep grassy slope to the south, grey limestones with scattered nodules of chert have yielded specimens of *Gigantoproductus giganteus*. This strongly ribbed productid holds the record for size amongst brachiopods throughout their long history. It was first described and figured by Martin in his *Petrificata Derbiensia* and the locality stated briefly was 'Buxton'. The author believes that Martin obtained his specimens from Holker Road in Buxton, for until a few years ago there was an excellent exposure there with large numbers of this fossil. The limestones containing *G. giganteus* in Buxton and in Miller's Dale are at roughly the same horizon; this fossil seems to be restricted to an horizon near the base of the D_2 zone. In the eastern part of the Wye Valley, roughly 200m of Viséan limestones intervene between the *G. giganteus* horizon and the local base of the Namurian. At Buxton, the Namurian rests almost directly upon this horizon, and this gives some measure not only of the incompleteness of the Lower Carboniferous succession on the western limb of the main anticline, but also of the extent of the pre-Namurian denudation of the Carboniferous Limestone in the west of the Peak District.

Hammerton Hill, a prominent feature to the north of the Wye east of Tideswell Dale, has a capping of white limestones, the Priestcliffe Beds. Beneath these on the steep western slope facing Tideswell Dale one can find small exposures of the Upper Lava; its thickness seems to be about twenty-five metres. When the lava outcrop is traced in an easterly direction on the hill slope above the school it is seen to thin rapidly and to die out in the same manner as was observed in the old railway cutting to the south (Figure 30).

On the north side of Hammerton Hill the outcrop of the Upper Lava is considerably displaced by a WNW–ESE fault which is seen to cut across Tideswell Dale. On the north side of this fault in Tideswell Dale is a complex inlier involving the Lower Lava and several

Fig 30   Hammerton Hill, Miller's Dale looking across the valley of the Wye from the south. The outcrop of the Upper Lava dying out here is indicated with broken lines and is marked by scattered small thorn bushes. Tideswell Dale is on the left; Tideswell Dale Quarry is visible in the middle distance. Part of the Namurian 'rim' at Rushup Edge forms the skyline on the left

Fig 31   Typical spheroidal weathering of basaltic lava (toadstone): Lower Lava,
Tideswell Dale, Derbyshire

intrusive sills. Many of the associated limestones are strongly
marmorised. The large quarry on the east side of Tideswell Dale
south of the picnic area shows a floor of strongly marmorised
limestone which was worked many years ago for marble. Above this is
a face of Lower Lava (Figure 31). At the southern edge of the quarry
the lava is seen to be underlain by one to two metres of indurated
purplish-red clay, a volcanic ash, which has been baked by the heat of
the succeeding lava so that it breaks into long prismatic columns
(Figure 32).

To the east of the line along which the Upper Lava dies out the
Miller's Dale Limestones are succeeded disconformably by the
Station Quarry Beds which pass up into similar thinly bedded dark-
grey limestones, with nodular and tabular chert. The lava horizon is
marked by a thin band of clay, a decomposed tuff. The higher
Priestcliffe Beds also change in character from being thickly bedded
light-grey limestones in the west, to becoming thinner-bedded and
darker-coloured in the east. The result is that, to the east of Litton
Mill, the landscape is moulded out of a rather monotonous series of

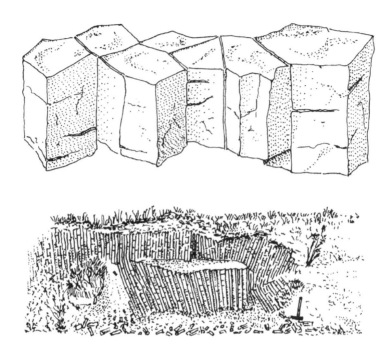

Fig 32   Clay rendered columnar through contact metamorphism by overlying lava flow, south end of Tideswell Dale Quarry, Tideswell Dale, Derbyshire. Lower sketch, temporary section; upper sketch, portions of columns, natural size

grey and dark-grey limestones with chert, having a thickness of about 200m, which have been called the Monsal Dale Beds. They do, however, include two horizons which can be traced over a large area, the Hobs House Coral Band which will be described later, and an extraordinary bed about two metres thick composed almost entirely of waterworn *Productus* valves. Both horizons afford evidence of very shallow water conditions.

The rather desolate slopes of Burfoot are underlain by these limestones. They are cut by two major mineral veins or rakes, the Burfoot Rake and the Putty Hill (or Putwell Hill) Rake, both running in a ENE–WSW direction. The Burfoot Rake, which was worked for galena, has some open works on the steep hillside to the south of

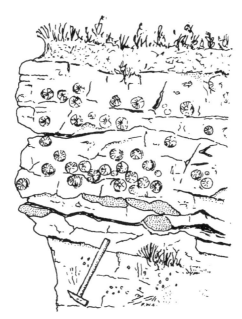

Fig 33 Exposure of the White Cliff Coral Band north of Little Longstone. Chert nodules are finely dotted. Notice colonial corals such as *Lithostrotion junceum* and *Syringopora* spp. in the lower part of the band by the hammer, and the simple or solitary corals (mainly clisiophyllids) in the upper part

Litton Mill from which good specimens of calcite can be collected. The Putty Hill Rake is easily traced over Putwell Hill to the south of the confluence of Hay Dale with Monsal Dale; it was formerly worked for galena, but more recently the calcite gangue was worked at the Monsaldale Spar Mine for use in stucco for houses.

The walk along that part of the Wye Valley from Litton Mill to Cressbrook Mill, often known as Water-cum-Jolly Dale, is one of the most attractive in the whole of the Peak District. The meander-like course of the river is deeply entrenched in the white-weathering Miller's Dale Beds giving vertical cliffs especially on the right bank. The Lower Lava can not lie very far below the surface for it peeps up just to the east of Litton Mill at river-level.

East of Cressbrook Mill, the valley assumes a different aspect, becoming more open as the somewhat more thinly bedded limestones above the Upper Lava horizon descend to river-level on the gentle easterly dip. Meadows are developed on a narrow flood-plain and for the first time in its course from Buxton the Wye includes a small farm in its valley.

Towards the southern end of Hay Dale bluffs of well bedded limestone with chert yield numerous fossils, including the coral *Lonsdaleia floriformis* (Figure 13, p 31) which indicates the D_2 zone. A disused quarry on the south side of the railway near the site of the former Monsal Dale Station gives a good section of these beds and yields a large productid fauna. On the opposite side of the river is White Cliff which exposes a well developed coral band with *Lithostrotion* spp. more or less in the growth position in the lower part, and a profusion of simple clisiophyllid corals in the upper part, most of them being in a recumbent position (Figure 33).

Coral bands of more limited extent occur in lower strata, especially

Fig 34   Hobs House, Monsal Dale. Slipped stacks of D_2 limestones with chert nodules. The Hobs House Coral Band is a short distance above the hammer on the right

in the Chee Tor and Miller's Dale Limestones which occur in the D_1 zone, but the White Cliff Coral Band is the one seen to greatest advantage in this traverse through the Wye Valley. Coral bands afford valuable evidence on the environmental conditions under which the limestones were laid down. Modern reef-building corals require warm, saline, shallow-water conditions so that they are within reach of sunlight, and an absence of mud. Certainly the limestones associated with these coral bands have a very low content of terrigenous mud so that the sea must have been clear. That it was warm and saline might be assumed merely on account of the existence of corals, though it must be stressed that these Carboniferous corals are extinct forms. The fact is that there is nothing in the limestones to suggest anything but clear shallow water.

Another well marked coral band may be examined on the left bank

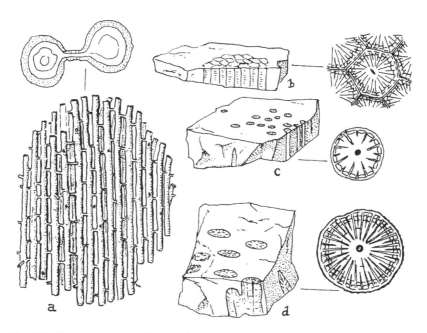

Fig 35 Some common Carboniferous Limestone corals. a, *Syringopora* cf *reticulata*; b, *Lithostrotion maccoyanum*; c. *L. junceum*; d, *L. irregulare*. Half natural size with enlarged insets

of the Wye, to the south of the Monsal Dale viaduct, at Hobs House, a collection of slipped limestone stacks (Figure 34). Here the limestones are medium-bedded rather dark-grey limestones with nodular and bedded chert. The corals in the band are silicified (Figure 35); that is, the calcium carbonate of the corals has been replaced by silica, and may be dissolved out of the matrix by placing a piece of coral-bearing limestone in a bath of dilute hydrochloric acid. The precise position of the Hobs House Coral Band is not known, but it probably lies not very far above the horizon of the Upper Lava. Hobs House is best approached by a footpath leaving the road just to the south of the Monsal Head Hotel and running high up the hillside above the west portal of the Headstone Tunnel to the east of the viaduct.

THE MASSIF FACIES

This section along the valley of the River Wye may be taken as the standard section of the Carboniferous Limestone for the Peak District. The succession of about 800m of limestones with several ash bands and lava flows in the middle part is very gently folded; the limestones are of shallow-water origin and are characterised by the presence of brachiopods and corals, and there is evidence in potholed and channeled surfaces not only of halts in subsidence of the basement during deposition, but of occasional reverse or upward movements. Deposition of such a succession appears to have taken place on a relatively rigid basement or massif. The type of sedimentation or facies may thus be referred to as the massif or block facies. It will be seen that the Derbyshire block in the northern part of the Peak District is roughly coincident in its boundaries with the present edge of the limestone area. Outside the rigid block in Lower Carboniferous times the sea was deeper and subsidence was more rapid than on the block. Terrigenous muds were brought into these deeper basin areas so that shales occur with muddy limestones. These conditions were inimical to the growth of reef-building corals, and goniatites and bivalves were the predominant elements of the fauna. Consequently, the basin facies can not be

Fig 36   Strip fields and limestone walls near Litton north of Miller's Dale. Hucklow Edge, part of the Namurian 'rim' on the skyline to the right

zoned by means of the corals and brachiopods which are so useful on the shelf.

In the Headstone cutting of the former main-line railway east of the Monsal Dale viaduct is a series of thinly bedded limestones with chert in which shale partings become thicker and more frequent to the east. These beds (Ashford Beds) are the highest in the Wye Valley section, and indeed the highest in the Dinantian. Some of the limestones contain *Spirifer* spp. and a bed of grey shale yields the goniatite *Goniatites granosus*. There are no longer any reef-building corals, the limestones are impure, and the shales are terrigenous muds. These highest beds were deposited in deeper water than any so far seen in the Wye Valley. A little farther to the east they are succeeded by shales of Namurian age with no suggestion of the unconformity so noticeable on the western limb of the main anticline near Buxton.

CHAPTER 6

The Valley of the River Goyt

At Burbage to the south-west of Buxton well bedded limestones in the D_1 zone of the Dinantian are seen dipping westwards at an angle of about 20°: the best exposures are near Grin on the east side of the Buxton–Leek road just to the north of the old-lime-waste tips. The field-walls in the immediate vicinity are of white-weathering lime-stone similar to those throughout the Carboniferous Limestone terrain of the Peak District. To the west of the main road is a descent to one of the headstreams of the River Wye along the banks of which grey and blue shales are exposed. The Limestones can be seen to dip beneath the shales.

The shales are the basal beds of a series of sandstones and shales which form Burbage Edge and the country to the west of this. Within this series of sandstones and shales are bands of shale with goniatites and other marine fossils, and occasional thin coal seams in the higher

Fig 37   A millstone. The Peak District National Park emblem

part of the succession. The higher sandstones are frequently coarse feldspathic sandstones to which the term 'grit' has often been applied. It is more satisfactory to refer to these grits as sandstones and to use qualifying adjectives, eg coarse feldspathic sandstone. These sandstones sometimes reach a thickness of thirty metres; they are often cross-bedded or flaggy, but some horizons yield a stone which is virtually a freestone, that is it can be worked equally well in all directions on account of its homogeneity. Such sandstones have been worked until recent years for kerbstones, setts, and building stone. In the past they have been used for the production of querns, and later for millstones. The modern roadside sign showing the boundary of the Peak District National Park is a millstone (Figure 37).

MILLSTONE GRIT AND NAMURIAN

It was on account of the production of millstones that early geologists, working in the Pennines, called this series of sandstones and shales, succeeding the Carboniferous Limestones, the Millstone Grit. In many ways, the name is an unfortunate one. First, shales and mudstones predominate over coarse sandstones particularly in the lower part of the series, and the term Millstone Grit in consequence is misleading. Secondly, the term does not refer to a single lithological type. Thirdly, and most important, the series is not of the same age throughout its development. It is a diachronous series, and so the term Millstone Grit has no strict stratigraphical meaning. At the time when the Dinantian limestones of the Peak District were being deposited in a warm shallow sea, a land area existed to the north of the Midland Valley of Scotland. Rivers and streams carried sand and mud into the shallows of the Dinantian sea in the midland valley area; this resulted in a series of sandstones and shales similar to the Millstone Grit of the Pennines. We thus reach the impossible situation where 'Millstone Grit' is of Carboniferous Limestone age.

It is for this reason that the term 'Millstone Grit' has been replaced by 'Namurian', named from Namur in Belgium where beds of this age are splendidly exposed along the valley of the River Meuse.

The upper and lower limits of the Namurian have been agreed

internationally and are defined palaeontologically. The rapidly
evolving goniatites which occur in discrete bands, the so-called
'marine bands' provide not only this definition but afford a means of
zoning. A great deal of the pioneer work on the Namurian goniatites
was carried out by W. S. Bisat in Britain, and the zonal scheme has
been well tried and improved by geologists in the British Geological
Survey and by a host of independent research-workers in Britain,
Belgium, France and Germany. The zonal scheme for the Namurian
is shown in Appendix V.

It can not be too strongly stressed that goniatites were by no means
confined to the Namurian. They first appeared in Devonian times,

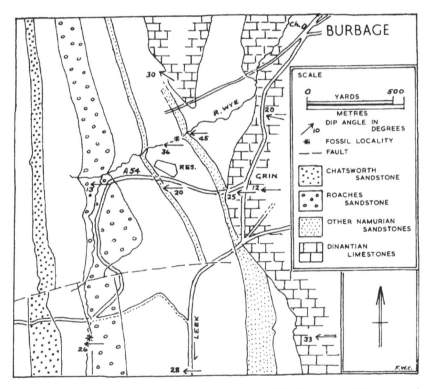

Fig 38   Geological sketch-map of the area west of Burbage and Grin south of
Buxton. Reduced from author's six-inch map. *Crown Copright reserved*

and under suitable environmental conditions flourished throughout the Lower Carboniferous. They are not found in the Lower Carboniferous massif facies in the Peak District possibly because the seas were too shallow, but we do find goniatites entering near the top of the sequence (p 71), the goniatite-bivalve faunas replacing the normal brachiopod-coral faunas of the earlier part of the Dinantian sequence.

Throughout the Lower Carboniferous there were certain marine areas of long and continued subsidence, accompanied by the deposition of terrigenous muds, where goniatites and bivalves were the main elements of the faunas. Consequently, there are two parallel zonal schemes for the Lower Carboniferous rocks, one based upon the corals and brachiopods, the other on the goniatites and bivalves. The approximate correlation of the two schemes is shown in Appendix II.

PRE-NAMURIAN DENUDATION

We have already seen that the beautiful valley of the River Wye from Buxton through Chee Dale and Miller's Dale to Little Longstone cuts through the major anticline affecting this part of the Peak District. The crest of this anticline can be located quite easily by observing from the Buxton–Bakewell main road how the westerly dip of the limestones continues as far as Woo Dale, six kilometres to the east of Buxton, beyond which an easterly dip sets in. The crest of this structure, marked by horizontality of the strata, lies at the confluence of Woo Dale with the main valley. The average rate of dip on the two limbs of the fold does not exceed $5°$ and so the anticline is more or less symmetrical in a geometrical sense. However, one has to travel about twice the distance on the eastern limb to reach the junction between the Carboniferous Limestone and the basal blue shales of the overlying Namurian, as compared with the western limb.

This is precisely because there is a more or less complete succession from the dolomitised limestones of the S_2 zone (as seen at Woo Dale and the foot of Topley Pike) through the D_1 and D_2 limestones and their associated volcanic rocks to the base of the

Namurian on the eastern limb of the anticline. On the western limb of the structure, the Namurian shales lie unconformably upon limestones at about the horizon of the Upper Lava so well seen on the eastern limb in Miller's Dale. Undoubtedly, the pile of Lower Carboniferous sediments in the Buxton area was just as complete in pre-Namurian times as on the eastern limb of the anticline. The removal of these sediments in the west must have been due to a pre-Namurian uplift and denudation, while gentle subsidence and deposition continued in the east.

The incompleteness of the succession in the west of the Peak District is even more extensive than would appear at first sight. In the east, the highest beds of the Dinantian are succeeded by the lowest beds of the Namurian without visible break. At Burbage reservoir near Buxton in the west, a Namurian marine band of R_2 age can be seen only a few metres above the denuded top of the limestones. In other words, not only was nearly half the thickness of limestones denuded in the west, but because the uplifted limestones were undergoing sub-aerial denudation, further deposition of sediments did not occur until Namurian time was well advanced.

This state of affairs is in remarkable contrast not only with that around Little Longstone and Bakewell, but also with that in the Mam

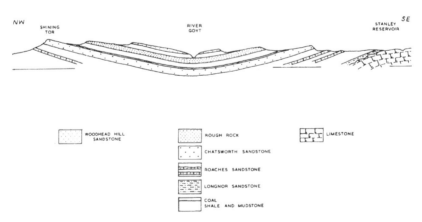

Fig 39 Sketch section across the Goyt Syncline. Total length of section approximately 7km. Datum line at 330m above sea-level

Tor–Kinder Scout area about fifteen kilometres to the north-east of Buxton where the Namurian sequence may be almost complete in some places.

THE GOYT SYNCLINE

The Namurian marine band, which crops out in the bed of the small stream alongside Burbage reservoir, contains the goniatite *Reticuloceras bilingue*. The Namurian strata above this marine band form the rising ground and boggy moorland country to the west of Buxton and Burbage. The beds are folded into a broad but marked syncline known as the Goyt Syncline because the River Goyt, forming the boundary between the counties of Cheshire and Derbyshire along much of its course, flows northwards approximately along the N–S axis of the fold (Figure 39).

The synclinal structure is very evident in the field, in fact it affords one of the most splendid examples in Britain of the relationship between structure and scenery. In one way the relationship is unusual because a major valley more or less coincides with the syncline. So often, the more tightly compressed rocks in the central part of a syncline give rise, after denudation, to hilly or mountainous country, a good example being the Snowdon area of North Wales. The reason for the valley-syncline relationship in the area of the River Goyt seems to lie in the way rocks of varying resistance to denudation succeed one another. The upper Namurian strata containing thick sandstones form a resistant framework to the syncline; they are succeeded by the much less resistant Westphalian (Coal Measures) strata which are predominantly shaly. Denudation has completely stripped the Coal Measures from the anticlines, and for the most part has scooped it out of the Goyt Syncline.

The limbs of the syncline have also been denuded so that if, for example, we travel from Burbage along the main road which leads to Congleton and Macclesfield, we ascend a series of steps marking the outcrops of the sandstones in the Namurian. The face of each step, which may be up to thirty metres in height, frequently provides exposures of the sandstone. The top of this escarpment or scarp is

Fig 40   Converging dip-slopes. The valley of the River Goyt looking northwards from the Macclesfield–Buxton road 2km east of the Cat and Fiddle Inn. The river approximately follows the axis of the Goyt Syncline

usually very sharp and forms a clear feature which can be traced across the landscape. In the Peak District it is frequently termed an 'edge', eg Drystone Edge, Axe Edge. The tread of the step usually slopes; it marks the outcrop of shales and mudstones between the sandstones. If the tread slopes in the direction of the dip of the beds and at approximately the same angle it is called a dip-slope (Figure 40).

The area of the Goyt Syncline is marked by inwardly inclined dip-slopes and outward facing scarps or 'edges' running roughly parallel to the N–S axis of the fold. It is an area of typical Pennine moorland rising to a height of 560m above sea-level at the Cat and Fiddle Inn on the western limb of the fold. The rocks are largely covered by thick deposits of moorland peat; judging from flint flakes which have been found at the base of the peat in various parts of the Pennines, this deposit appears to have formed mainly since Mesolithic times. It frequently has boles and trunks of trees, mainly birch, at the base, and is now being eroded very rapidly particularly along stream courses. The moorland vegetation in the areas of thick ill-drained peat, usually over shales and mudstones, consists of tussock grass, cotton-grass, heather, bilberry, reeds and sedges. On the sandstone outcrops the peat is usually thinner or absent, the drainage is better and the reeds and sedges are replaced by bracken.

Apart from sheep-grazing and grouse-shooting, this moorland country, which can be very inhospitable during the winter months, is not used. The few meadows and pastures which once existed along the flood-plain of the River Goyt have been submerged by the construction of reservoirs to supply Stockport with water. Several cottages existed near the head of the river east of the Cat and Fiddle Inn prior to the construction of the reservoirs. They were probably built to house miners who, up to about the end of the 19th century, worked some of the thin seams of coal in the outlier of Lower Coal Measures on Goyt's Moss. The coal, which is not of good quality, was sent to various parts of the Peak District for the 'burning' of limestone to produce quicklime.

Some of the Namurian sandstones have been worked in the past, though the only major quarry was at Goyt's Clough where building stone was worked in the topmost sandstone of the Namurian, generally referred to as the Rough Rock.

The only main road across the Goyt area is that which runs from Buxton to Macclesfield. Prior to the use of snow ploughs its course was marked by wooden poles, for snowfalls can be heavy on this high ground.

The Upper Namurian succession on the eastern limb of the Goyt Syncline can be examined by following the Buxton–Macclesfield road in a westerly direction from its junction with the main road to Leek. The lowest major sandstone is met where the road takes a sharp bend to the left; the rocks are poorly exposed here, but the grass and

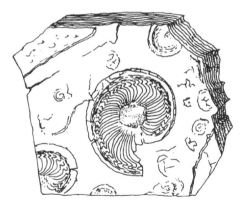

Fig 41 *Reticuloceras superbilingue.* Crushed specimen in shale displaying typical ornamentation. Natural size

bracken-clothed scarp can be traced with ease across country to the north and south. This Roaches Sandstone develops a well-marked partly peat-covered dip-slope to the south of a point where a cart-track from the Buxton–Leek road joins the Macclesfield road. The top of the sandstone may be seen in the bed of a small northerly-flowing stream on the south side of the main road at a point marked by a Buxton Corporation pumping station. The sandstone is seen to be succeeded by a marine band which contains the goniatite *Reticuloceras superbilingue* in abundance (Figure 41). The marine band is seen to be followed by unfossiliferous shales and mudstones in the slope to the west of the stream, and these shales are capped by the next higher sandstone which forms another marked scarp. At this particular point the sandstone is grotesquely weathered to produce the well known Toad Rock.

If we climb the scarp of this sandstone we find a dip-slope developed, but exposures of the sandstone are poor owing to the presence of peat, and the overlying beds are not exposed at all. However, where the dip-slope flattens out to the west there are several heaps of weathered shale obviously derived from some ancient filled-in shafts. Fragments of coal occur in the heaps, and careful

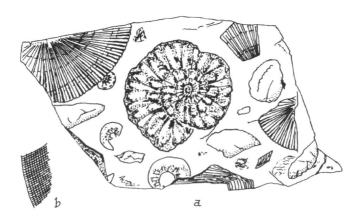

Fig 42 *Gastrioceras cancellatum* Bisat. a, typical specimen from *G. cancellatum* marine band, natural size; b, the ornamentation of the goniatite ×10

examination will result in the finding of the goniatite *Gastrioceras cancellatum* (Figure 42). The marine band is not exposed *in situ* but when we visit Goldsitch Moss, farther south in the Goyt Syncline, we shall find a coal seam over a metre thick between this marine band and the underlying sandstone. Clearly this coal was worked many years ago on Goyt's Moss. The old coal shafts are located in a belt of boggy ground, marking the outcrop of shales above the marine band, about 100m wide. On the western side of this ill-drained ground a slight rise marks the outcrop of a further sandstone formation; it is poorly exposed, but can be traced by feature northwards into the valley of the River Goyt where it is seen to be succeeded by a fireclay up to two metres in thickness, a very thin coal, and a marine band, a bed of blue-grey and black shale with an intersecting marine fauna including the goniatite *Gastrioceras subcrenatum*. This marine band is the internationally accepted boundary between the Namurian (Millstone Grit) and Westphalian (Coal Measures). The sandstone below it is the Rough Rock, the highest sandstone formation in the Namurian.

On the eastern limb of the Goyt Syncline the Rough Rock is followed by shales and then by another sandstone the equivalent of the Woodhead Hill Sandstone of Lancashire.

The succession described so far can be recognised quite easily on the western limb of the syncline. It is risky to attempt a correlation of the sandstones on the two limbs on lithological grounds alone; indeed, the only safe method of correlation is by means of the goniatites in the marine bands above the sandstones.

The Woodhead Hill Sandstone which we saw on the eastern limb of the syncline can be recognised on the western limb as the sandstone on which the Cat and Fiddle Inn is built. The Namurian sandstones on that limb form westerly-facing scarps to the west of the inn. The Woodhead Hill Sandstone forms a long peat-covered dip-slope running eastwards from the inn down into the headstream of the River Goyt. In the bed of the stream the top of this sandstone is seen to be flaggy, with well formed ripple marks on some of the bedding planes. The top of the sandstone contains roots of *Stigmaria* and is a ganister; this is the seat-earth to a coal of poor quality about

Fig 43   Non-marine bivalves from shale above the Goyt's Coal at Goyt's Moss, Cheshire. Natural size. a, *Carbonicola* cf *fallax* Wright; b, *C.* cf *obliqua* Wright

two metres thick which is exposed from time to time at the point where the easterly flowing headstream of the Goyt turns abruptly northwards. The coal, the equivalent of the Bassy Mine of Lancashire, consists of innumerable laminae of coal and carbonaceous shale with fossil plants. Its roof is of blue shales and mudstones with non-marine bivalves, species of *Carbonicola* and *Anthracosia* (Figure 43) at various horizons which permit a correlation with coals in the Lancashire, Cheshire, and North Staffordshire coalfields. Above this coal at Goyt's moss are several scores of metres of higher beds, mainly shales and a highly quartzose ganister, which are poorly exposed.

Here at Goyt's Moss is a small isolated coalfield, an outlier of lowest Westphalian or Coal Measures. The so-called 'Goyt's coal' was worked many years ago to be carried by horse-drawn vehicles to Buxton and other places for the 'burning' of limestone. This thin veneer of Coal Measures rocks is all that remains of a former cover of up to 3,000m of Coal Measures, including up to 100m of coal in some dozens of seams, which formerly stood above Goyt's Moss and which was largely removed by denudation in pre-Triassic times.

It is well worthwhile walking down the valley of the River Goyt from Goyt's Moss. Very quickly the river as it flows northwards cuts down into the Rough Rock and it is this sandstone which forms crags on either side as far as the old Goyt's Clough quarry which lies approximately on the axis of the syncline.

NAMURIAN CYCLIC SEDIMENTATION

In traversing the Namurian succession exposed between Burbage and Goyt's Moss it quickly becomes apparent that beds of different lithology follow one another in no haphazard fashion but in a specific order repeated time after time. A thick sandstone is succeeded by a seat-earth and a thin coal. Above the coal is a band of shale with marine fossils followed by a thickness of unfossiliferous shales and mudstones often with ironstone nodules in the upper part. Then follows the next thick sandstone and another cyclic unit or 'cyclothem' (Figure 44).

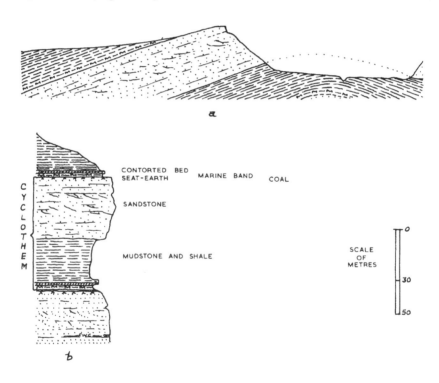

Fig 44   An Upper Namurian cyclothem; a, showing the relationship of surface slope to the lithological units of the cyclothem; b, a vertical section showing a typical cyclothem

There have been many hypotheses to account for cyclic deposition but none has been generally accepted or can be proved. A simple case of cyclic deposition involves two lithologies, a good example being the monotonous repetition of thin beds of limestone and shale as in the Lias of Dorset. More complicated and the best example in Britain is the cyclic sequence in the Yoredale (Lower/Upper Carboniferous) Series in north Yorkshire. A limestone with marine fossils is followed by shales with marine fossils, unfossiliferous shales, sandstone, seat-earth and coal. This constitutes a cyclic unit or cyclothem; the coal at the top of one cyclothem is succeeded by the limestone of the next higher cyclothem (Figure 45).

In the Upper Namurian beds of the Goyt Trough the thick sandstones are frequently feldspathic or arkosic and have clearly been derived from a granite terrain; parts of the sandstones show well marked cross-bedding. Studies of this cross-bedding strongly suggest deposition by strong streams and rivers possibly braided or mean-dering over alluvial deposits leading out to deltas in the Namurian sea. Undoubtedly the area was subsiding but eventually sedimenta-tion overtook subsidence and sand and mud banks rose above water-

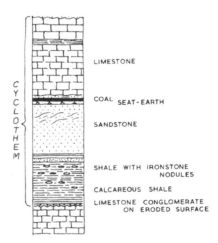

Fig 45   A typical Yoredale cyclothem. Thicknesses vary considerably but the approximate scale here is 1cm to 1m

level. Plants, some such as *Lepidodendron* of considerable height, colonised these low banks; a bed of peat was formed from their decaying remains and this was later transformed into coal.

Continued subsidence or possibly accelerated subsidence allowed the sea to sweep over vast areas bringing the growth of peat to an end. The deepening sea contained a fauna of bivalves, goniatites which were probably free-swimming organisms, and fish. Carbonaceous muds containing these organisms were deposited slowly to form a marine band. At this stage there was a withdrawal of the sea as the area again came under the influence of rivers flowing mainly from the north. First muds were deposited, and later there was an advance of immense loads of sandy debris which were to form the next body of sandstone.

It is the repetition of such a sequence of processes which is so difficult to explain. The possibility of eustatic changes of sea-level as a result of happenings in other parts of the world can not be ruled out. In late Carboniferous time the area of the British Isles lay within the equatorial zone. About the same time in the southern hemisphere there is abundant evidence of an ice age, and it has been suggested that the repeated depletion and accretion of ice could result in changes of sea-level (eustatic changes) which might have resulted in the numerous marine transgressions, marked by marine bands, in our Upper Carboniferous rocks. However, the multiplicity of cyclothems in these rocks does make such an explanation rather difficult to accept. Apart from the small thickness of lowest Coal Measures strata in the Goyt Syncline, which is the maximum for the Peak District as a whole, we are not here concerned with the thousands of metres of Coal Measures strata which have been stripped off the area. Nevertheless, it is useful to notice that in the adjacent coalfields of Lancashire and Cheshire, North Staffordshire, and Derbyshire some dozens of cyclothems are present. The marine phase is not always present, its place above a coal seam often being taken by a shale or mudstone with non-marine bivalves of which we have had an example in the case of the roof of the Goyt's Coal. A satisfactory hypothesis for cyclic sedimentation must be able to account for the production of several dozens of cyclothems in the Upper Carboniferous of Britain.

CONTORTED BEDS

The Upper Namurian marine bands are all exposed in the Goyt Syncline but the best localities are somewhat inaccessible.

Perhaps the most important one is the *Gastrioceras subcrenatum* band just above the Rough Rock, for this is the agreed boundary between the Namurian and Westphalian.

The top of the Rough Rock and the beds immediately above it are exposed from time to time in Deep Clough, about 340m south of Goyt's Clough quarry. The section is as follows:

	Metres
Cross-bedded sandstone (Woodhead Hill Sst)	—
Blue and grey shales	15
Contorted blue shale	0.5
Marine band (*G. subcrenatum*)	0.4
Shale	0.3
Coal	0.05
Fireclay and ganister	1.5
Pale-grey sandstone (Rough Rock)	—

The contorted blue shale immediately above the marine band is of considerable interest. It consists of a discrete bed with slickensides in

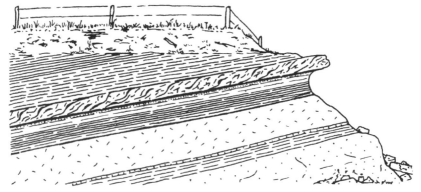

Fig 46   Contorted bed above a Namurian marine band. The axis of the syncline lies to the left

the direction of dip on the upper and lower surfaces, evidence of differential movement along the bedding, or 'bedding-plane slip'. Internally, the laminations of the original shale are completely disturbed by curved highly-polished slip-planes and small inclined folds, the axial planes of the folds dipping towards the axis of the Goyt Syncline (Figure 46).

Similar contorted beds have been found above each of the other marine bands in the Goyt Syncline and in other areas where the strata have an appreciable dip. In fact, there is at least one contorted band in the shaly strata between each pair of major sandstones; the contorted bed in each cyclothem is normally immediately above the marine band. Since a contorted bed is easily spotted in the field, especially in a stream section, it is the most useful guide in the location of the associated marine band.

These contorted beds are believed to have been produced during the folding of the rocks. The Upper Namurian rocks are like a multiple sandwich in which the slices of bread are represented by the major sandstones, and the fillings take the form of the argillaceous beds between the sandstones. Sandstones are strong rocks which can transmit stress during folding; they are spoken of as 'competent' rocks. The intervening shales on the other hand are weak or 'incompetent' rocks which tend to accommodate themselves to the sandstones during folding. If you take a thick book with a flexible back and bend it into an anticline or syncline you will quickly observe

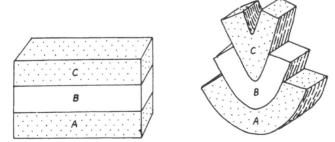

Fig 47   Bedding-plane slip produced when a pile of sediments A, B, and C is folded. The slip will be zero along the axis of the fold

that in the process of folding the leaves slide over one another (Figure 47). It is believed that something similar happens during the folding of an alternation of competent and incompetent strata.

The beds slide over one another but the major sliding is concentrated in the least competent beds which generally lie immediately above the marine bands in the Namurian. It might be thought that the marine bands, which are usually so soft and friable in the field, are the weakest beds, but it seems likely that they are not so incompetent prior to their decalcification at the surface.

CHAPTER 7

Castleton, Edale and Mam Tor

The village of Castleton is situated on the northern edge of the limestone area of the Peak District. To the north is the Edale valley, excavated in the Namurian shales and subsidiary sandstones which succeed the northerly-dipping limestones and backed by the plateau-like bastion, composed largely of thick sandstones, which culminates in the Peak or Kinder Scout. The village derives its name from Peveril Castle, an eleventh-century fortification placed in an almost impregnable position on the south side of the village.

Castleton is a popular area on account both of its attractive scenery in the Dinantian limestones and in the Namurian sandstones, and of its caves, a number of which are artifically lighted and open to the public. The area was formerly important for the mining of galena, and many old opencast workings can be examined; it is now important for the production of cement thanks to the juxtaposition of suitable limestones and Namurian mudstones.

Away to the west the landscape is dominated by Mam Tor, a little over two kilometres from Castleton (Figure 48). Mam Tor is known

Fig 48   Mam Tor viewed from the south; landslip scar in Mam Tor Beds

89

also as the 'shivering mountain'. It is a large landslip scar in Namurian shales, and the considerable area of hummocky pasture to the east below it represents material which has slipped from its face over the centuries. The hill is still unstable and, as the slipped material is lubricated with water from springs, the main road below Mam Tor posed a difficult problem and was closed in 1977.

In approaching the Castleton area from the south we traverse a high rather bleak limestone plateau partitioned into large fields by old limestone walls, with here and there a small overgrown quarry from which walling-stone was obtained, and sometimes lines of overgrown depressions and hummocks marking the outcrop of mineral veins. There are small isolated walled plantations of beech, and farmhouses are very scattered. The thin grey soil and the altitude are not conducive to the production of arable crops, and it is no easy matter in this terrain to produce the hay necessary to sustain cattle during the winter months.

Wherever the underlying limestones can be examined they are seen to be similar to those exposed in the valley of the Wye, gently dipping well-bedded limestones often poorly fossiliferous apart from the ubiquitous crinoid ossicles, but occasionally with a band of corals.

This massif facies of the Dinantian can be traced to the beautiful gorge known as the Winnats to the west of Castleton and as far as Cave Dale to the south of the village (Figure 49). Here there is an

Fig 49   Cavedale; north end with Peveril Castle on the left

outcrop of a thin amygdaloidal basaltic lava which can be correlated with the Lower Lava of Miller's Dale because bands with *Davidsonina septosa* occur beneath it, in limestones which have lithological similarities with the Chee Tor Beds.

A splendid view of the Edale valley and Castleton may be had from the old road below Mam Tor. From here the limestone is seen to form a steep northward-facing slope and the junction with the overlying Namurian shales is approximately at the foot of this slope. Nowhere on the limestone slope is it possible to find the well bedded limestones which can be seen a short distance to the south of it, as in Cave Dale.

REEF LIMESTONES

A closer examination may be made in the deep valley on the south side of the main road at Mam Tor and a little to the east of the Blue John Cavern. The basal Namurian beds, known as the Edale Shales, are seen to rest upon an eroded surface of the limestone. The limestone is very fine-grained, almost a calcilutite; bedding planes are absent or obscure, and although much of the rock is virtually unfossiliferous there are patches or pockets of beautifully preserved fossils, especially brachiopods. Corals are infrequent. Such limestones are known as 'reef' limestones.

Reef limestones are by no means confined to the Carboniferous, but much of the pioneer work on reef limestones was carried out in the British Carboniferous, especially in the Craven area of Yorkshire and the Clitheroe area of Lancashire where the reefs form knoll-like hills. These reefs are seen to be surrounded by well bedded limestones such as are seen in Miller's Dale. Each reef is a buried mound of almost unbedded limestone though there may be outward-directed and concentric partings giving the appearance of quaquaversal dips. Some early workers favoured a tectonic origin for these reefs; others favoured an origin as discrete mounds of calcareous mud on the sea floor. The latter view was more generally supported, though it was difficult to understand how a mound of almost impalpable calcareous mud could stand under water and maintain the steep slopes now observable. The other major question concerned the relation of the reef limestone to the bedded limestone surrounding it.

The reef limestones of Castleton though lithologically and palaeontologically similar to the Clitheroe reefs do not generally show the same mound-like form. Their precise relations to the bedded succession farther south have given rise to considerable discussion. It is now generally agreed that the bedded limestones of the massif pass northwards into reefs, and indeed this passage can be seen quite clearly in the Winnats.

Near the Blue John Cavern the reef limestones are highly fossiliferous, yielding a profusion of brachiopods (Figure 50), bryozoa, bivalves and gastropods, together with fragments of trilobites. Many fossils and cavities in the limestones were partly filled with sediment, the remainders of the voids being filled at a later date by calcite carried in by ground-waters (Figure 51). These partial infillings give a good indication of the plane of the horizontal at the time when they were made; they act as frozen-in spirit-levels. They indicate quite clearly that the present dip of these reef limestones is mainly a primary dip which means that these sediments accumulated

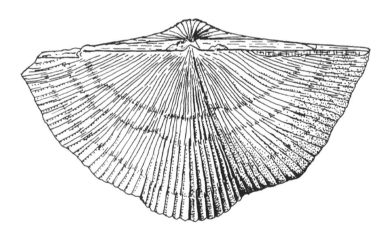

Fig 50   *Spirifer striatus* (Martin) from Nunlow Quarry near Castleton, natural size

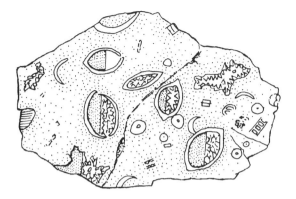

Fig 51 Polished surface of reef limestone showing brachiopods and cavities partly infilled with sediment (dotted), the remainder of each cavity being occupied by calcite or still empty. The specimen should be rotated anticlockwise 90° to be in its depositional position. Half natural size

upon a sloping sea-floor. The reef limestones show dips between 25°and 35°.

This type of reef has been called an apron-reef. It seems to be a marginal facies which developed between the shallow shelf area of the massif and a basin area of deeper water which lay to the north. The reef complex can be divided into a back reef nearest to the shelf area, a central algal reef, and a fore-reef nearest to the basin. The algal reef, sometimes as much as eighty metres in width, contains abundant stromatolitic algae. The fossils in the fore-reef show little or no evidence of abrasion through movement under the action of gravity or currents in spite of the steep slope of the sea bed. Goniatites occur in solid form in some of the reef limestones. At Cow Low Nick, a short distance south-east of the foot of the Winnats, there is a bed of fore-reef limestone with an abundance of goniatites which afford evidence of current action.

CAVES OF THE CASTLETON DISTRICT

The Castleton District has long been famous for its caverns. They are developed mainly in reef limestones though other features associated with an extensive system of underground drainage are present in the massif limestones also. Eldon Hole, three kilometres south-west of Castleton, is an immense pothole completely open at the surface; it is the largest open pothole in the Peak District having a depth of 80m and an orifice measuring 35m in length and 6m in width. The following caverns are open to the public:

Blue John Caverns   These are situated on the south side of the old road over Mam Tor. The entrance is artificial and, along with the chain of caverns open to the public, is well lighted. There are some good examples of Blue John, a purplish variety of fluor-spar, and stalactites and stalagmites.

Treak Cliff Cavern   The entrance is on Treak Cliff above the main road. The outer part of the entrance roadway is lined as it is cut through Edale conglomerate at the base of the Edale Shales consisting of large blocks of limestone with a shale matrix. Inside the entrance roadway, stairs and a footway lead to what are called the old series of caves, exposing a boulder bed of limestone blocks in a matrix of shale. Blue John veins are exposed here. A little further in, the caves are developed in the limestones beneath the boulder bed; the top of these limestones is fissured and many of the fissures are filled with Blue John and other minerals. There is an inner or new series of caverns with some of the best stalactites to be seen anywhere in the Peak District.

Speedwell Cavern   The entrance is at the foot of the Winnats and is artificial. A flight of steps leads down to the Grand Canal, a flooded straight mine drivage through limestone nearly 900m long. Visitors are taken along this by boat and then step out on to a platform to look down into the flooded Bottomless Pit in a lofty cavern. Tests have shown that the water in the Bottomless Pit reappears at Russet Well in Castleton nearly a kilometre to the east.

Peak Cavern   On the southern edge of Castleton village at the foot of a vertical cliff. The entrance, the largest cavern entrance in Britain, is impressive; it is 20m high, 33m wide and extends in for 108m. This large outer cavern was at one time used by ropemakers. There is a very extensive series of caverns many of which are open to visitors. A local legend holds that a goose seen to fall into Eldon Hole flew out of Peak Cavern, having lost its feathers on the long journey underground.

THE SPEEDWELL VENT

About 500m south-east of the Speedwell Cavern entrance and at the foot of the steep north-facing limestone slope there is a slight rise of ground with poor exposures of basaltic and pyroclastic material. It is probable that the exposures were better about the end of the last century for it was then identified as a vent with some confidence. It is called the Speedwell Vent, but until the mound has been explored with a borehole there can be no certainty that it marks the site of a vent. It might also represent material from the Lower Lava to the south which poured down the submarine slope formed of accumulating apron-reef.

FOSSILS OF THE REEF LIMESTONES

The apron-reef limestones can be seen to be continuous with the bedded limestones of the massif or shelf in several places, the Winnats undoubtedly affording the most continuous and convincing exposures. Without this type of visible continuity of the two facies correlation on palaeontological grounds would be a matter of considerable uncertainty. The brachiopod-coral faunas of the shelf limestones fail as the reef is approached. In the reef there is a markedly different fauna of brachiopods, bivalves, gastropods, bryozoa, goniatites, occasional fragments of trilobites, abundant algae and occasional sponges. The faunas are very specialised ones; in the brachiopods for example the genus *Pugnax* is abundantly represented by several species in the reef but is virtually unknown in the shelf limestones. In the latter, corals such as *Dibunophyllum, Palaeosmilia, Caninia, Lonsdaleia* and *Carcinophyllum* are well represented by a number of species depending upon horizon, while species of *Lithostrotion* are almost ubiquitous. In the reef limestones corals are extremely rare; they are usually species of *Lithostrotion* or of the strange *Amplexus*. Goniatites are virtually unknown in the shelf limestones.

The goniatites were quickly evolving cephalopods; their rapid vertical change, wide geographical distribution, relative abundance and ease of identification have allowed means of establishing a zonal scheme parallel to the coral-brachiopod zonation in the shelf limestones. The approximate equation of the two zonal schemes is given in Appendix VI.

The correlation of these two zonal schemes has been a matter of long-standing controversy and the equations shown in the Appendix are only very approximate. The P_1 zone has been sub-divided and there are still differences of opinion over the shelf facies equivalents of these subdivisions or subzones.

THE USE OF GONIATITES

The use of the goniatites as zone fossils has been invaluable in the classification of the Namurian strata, and indeed the lower and upper limits of the Namurian have been placed at the marine bands with *Cravenoceras leion* Bisat and *Gastrioceras subcrenatum* respectively. The zones of the Namurian are as follows:

> G *Gastrioceras*
> R *Reticuloceras*
> H *Homoceras*
> E *Eumorphoceras*

The *Gastrioceras* zone bridges the uppermost Namurian and lowest part of the Westphalian and has been subdivided. The other zones have also been subdivided, and it is through the careful zoning of the basal Namurian beds around the limestone of the Peak District that the magnitude or indeed the absence or presence of the Dinantian/ Namurian unconformity can be ascertained.

In 1945, Hudson and Cotton described the cores of a borehole put down to a depth of 230m in the Edale valley, upstream from Barber Booth Farm and about two kilometres north-west of Mam Tor. This borehole, known as the Edale borehole, began in E zone Namurian shales with the *Cravenoceras leion* fauna at a depth of 98m, this goniatite marking the base of the Namurian. Below this, the borehole was entirely in beds of Dinantian age of a lithology and with palaeontological characters quite different from the limestones deposited on the massif (shelf facies) or in the reefs (marginal facies). This third facies proved in the borehole consists of generally thin-bedded argillaceous, crinoidal, dolomitic and black carbonaceous limestones, with occasional chert, together with interbedded shales and mudstones. The fossils consist of brachiopods, zaphrentid corals and goniatites. There seems to have been almost continuous sedimentation from late Dinantian (Viséan) to early Namurian times.

THE NAMURIAN OF THE EDALE VALLEY

There are many interesting exposures of the Namurian shales, extending almost from the base of the E zone to the lower part of the R zone (Edale Shales), in the Edale valley. The flanks of this valley are deeply dissected by the River Noe and its numerous tributaries. The lowest beds exposed at the surface can be examined towards the western end of the valley near the Barber Booth railway viaduct (Figure 52). Some twenty-five metres of shale are exposed. Fossils are numerous and include *Cravenoceras malhamense* and *Neodimorphoceras scaliger* as well as bivalves including large examples of *Posidonia membranacea*. The succeeding beds in the upper part of the Eumorphoceras zone (E$_2$) are well represented around Upper Booth to the north-west of the confluence of the Crowden Brook with the River Noe. The fossils to be found here include species of *Eumorphoceras*, *Cravenoceratoides*, bivalves, brachiopods and trilobites. Higher up the valley of the River Noe near Lee House beds referable to the Homoceras zone are exposed. Strata belonging to the lower part of the Reticuloceras zone (R$_1$) are to be seen upstream of Lee House.

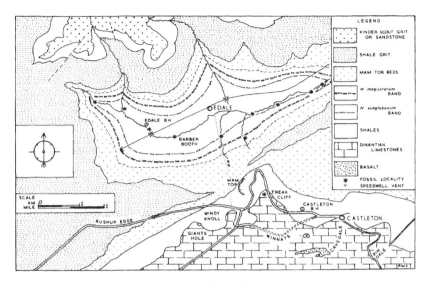

Fig 52   Geological sketch map of the Edale–Castleton area, Derbyshire. *Crown Copyright. Based on maps of the Geological Survey of Great Britain, and reproduced by permission of the Controller, Her Majesty's Stationery Office*

All around the Edale valley which cuts through an elongated dome in the Namurian strata, the Edale Shales (zones E_1 to R_1) are seen to be succeeded by a group of interbedded sandstones, siltstones and shales called the Mam Tor Beds on account of their good development at Mam Tor (Figure 52).

The vertical landslip scar on the south-eastern face of Mam Tor exposes at least 140m of alternating sandstones and shales included in the Mam Tor Beds. The average bed of sandstone shows graded bedding, that is the grain size decreases upwards from the base (Figure 53); on the underside are sole-structures such as flute-casts and groove-casts (Figure 54), and it is now generally agreed that these sandstones were deposited in quiet deep waters by turbidity currents, these currents originating in the slumping of deltaic sediments deposited higher on the submarine slopes. The intercalated grey shales contain thin-shelled marine bivalves.

Below the Mam Tor Beds are the Edale Shales, blue and black shales with layers of 'bullions' at several horizons. Many of the shales

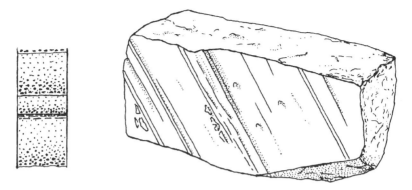

Fig 53 Graded bedding. The thicknesses can vary enormously from centimetres to metres

Fig 54 Groove-casts on the base of a bed of sandstone from the Mam Tor Beds at Mam Tor. The specimen is half a metre long

contain crushed goniatites and species of the bivalve *Dunbarella* (Figure 55), while the flint-hard bullions at a number of horizons yield fairly well-preserved solid goniatites. It is not possible to reach many of the fossiliferous horizons on the unstable face of Mam Tor, but slipped bullions can often be found in the landslip material. The fossils indicate that between Mam Tor and the Odin Fissure the

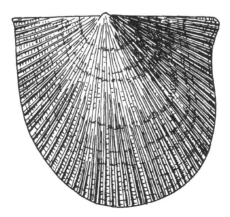

Fig 55 *Dunbarella* sp. Natural size for adult individual

Edale Shales, which have a thickness of about 130m here, range in age from basal R_1 just below the Mam Tor Beds to E_2 immediately above the limestone. It has already been stated that hereabouts the shales rest upon an eroded limestone surface. The reef limestones here have yielded goniatites indicating a B_2 age so that not only is the basal Namurian (including the *Cravenoceras leion* beds) missing, but the Posidonia zone at the top of the Viséan is absent owing to pre-Namurian erosion.

The junction between the Edale Shales and the limestone is of particular interest at Windy Knoll, a quarry lying a short distance south-west of the junction between the main road along Rushup Edge and the road to Sparrowpit. Here the limestone is exposed only through quarrying, though a pothole may have existed before the quarry was opened. The limestones are light-grey crinoidal beds of back-reef facies; there is a good fauna of reef brachiopods together with *Davidsonina septosa* and *Palaeosmilia murchisoni* (Figure 56) which are found in D_1 limestones of the shelf or massif facies. These limestones are traversed by several fissures filled with dark bituminous limestones similar in lithology to the Eyam Limestones which normally succeed the B_2 apron reef limestones in Castleton

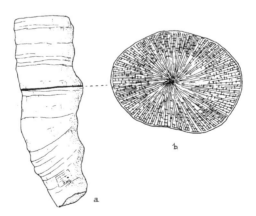

Fig 56 *Palaeosmilia murchisoni* (Edwards & Haime). D_1 limestones, near Castleton, Derbyshire. a, corallum half natural size; b, transverse section showing numerous thin septa and wide zone of dissepiments

Fig 57   The Kinder Scout plateau viewed from the south

and the country to the east. Such sedimentary infillings of fissures on the sea-floor are called Neptunian dykes. The top two metres of limestone are impregnated with viscous hydrocarbon elastic bitumen or elaterite, covered unconformably by the Namurian Edale Shales.

Edale valley, excavated in the Edale Shales and overlying Mam Tor Beds, appears fertile against the gaunt bastions rising into the pleateau of the Peak (Figure 57), composed largely of the Namurian Kinder Scout Grit, a coarse feldspathic sandstone. To the east is Win Hill, an outlier of these Kinder Scout Beds.

CHAPTER 8

Bradwell Dale and Eyam

The area between Hope, Great Hucklow, Eyam, and Hathersage is a superb one for walking; the scenery is constantly changing on account of the different rocks, limestones, sandstones, and shales which have contrasted types of weathering, and the geology is of considerable interest. Along with the Pindale region to the south-east of Castleton parts of the area, particularly near Bradwell and Eyam, have in the past been the scene of intense mining activity for lead, barytes and fluor-spar. It is possible that the mining of lead goes back to Roman times, for a Roman pig of lead was found at Bradwell in 1893. The village of Bradwell, particularly attractive at its southern end where houses are picturesquely perched on vertical or overhanging limestone crags is close to the old Roman station of Anavio near Brough. This station was connected to the Roman town of Aquae Arnemetiae (now Buxton) by the road known as Batham Gate, of which considerable relics still remain, and indeed some stretches of Batham Gate are followed by present-day roads as at Peak Dale north-east of Buxton and to the north-west of Bradwell village.

BRADWELL DALE

Bradwell, a typical Derbyshire village, stands at the northern end of Bradwell Dale which though barely a kilometre in length is an excellent example of a dry valley. This valley is followed by the road running southwards to Tideswell; it is bounded on both sides by towering cliffs of thickly bedded limestones modified in places by a certain amount of quarrying.

The limestones are almost horizontal and in many places can be examined in detail by climbing from one bedding plane to another. About 350m north of Hazlebadge Hall at the south end of the dale a

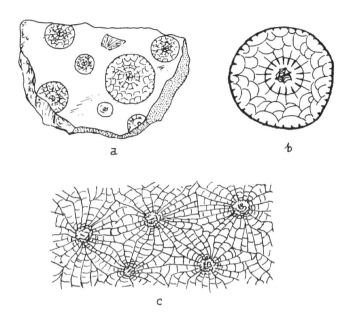

Fig 58 a, *Lonsdaleia duplicata*, D_2 zone, Monsal Dale, showing typical arrangement of corallites, half natural size; b, transverse section of a single corallite of *L. duplicata*, natural size; c, *Orionastraea* sp., twice natural size

mineral vein, the Earl Rake, crosses the dale; running in an ENE–WSW direction the walls of this rake show horizontal slickensides indicating that the mineralising fluids followed a fault, probably of small throw, in which the last movement was that usually associated with tear- or wrench-faulting. The Earl Rake carries zinc blende or sphalerite and can be traced laterally for a considerable distance.

Just to the north of the mineral vein on both sides of the dale pale-grey limestones with bedded and nodular chert contain fossils such as *Lonsdaleia duplicata* (Figure 58) typical of the Monsal Dale Beds (upper D_2 of the Wye Valley section). About twelve metres above the level of the road is a band of fossils including productids, species of *Lithostrotion* and *Orionastraea placenta* (Figure 58). Because of the presence of this last fossil the bed, which is about one metre thick, is called the *Orionastraea* band and is invaluable as a marker horizon. *Orionastraea* is a compound rugose coral similar to *Lithostrotion* in which the 'thecal' or boundary walls of the corallites have broken down and septa of adjacent corallites have joined together.

About twelve metres above the *Orionastraea* band is a conspicuous bedding plane and above this are reefy limestones of the Eyam Limestone group of Upper P_2 age. If, at this point, one views the exposures on the east side of the dale from the opposite side it can be seen that the Monsal Dale Beds have a gentle southerly dip whilst the Eyam Limestones are horizontal. The conspicuous bedding plane between the two groups of limestones is clearly an unconformable junction here. As the *Orionastraea* band is followed down the dale towards Bradwell village it is seen to get nearer and nearer to the plane of unconformity until close to the southern edge of the village it is cut by the unconformity. Northwards the Eyam Limestones lie upon horizons of the Monsal Dale Beds below the *Orionastraea* band. This unconformity is one of a number present in the marginal area of the Peak District limestone area and probably marks contemporaneous local uplift and erosion in the hinge, possibly fault-controlled, zone between the shelf and basin areas.

Although the main part of Bradwell Dale is a dry valley, just to the south of the village is a resurgence of water from the very extensive cavern system of the Castleton-Hope area. Almost five million gallons of water a day are obtained from this resurgence and that at Peak's Hole. This temporarily hard water is passed through filtration plants and pumped to the Ladybower Reservoir a short distance to the north. There it is a useful and beneficial addition to the soft slightly acid water brought in by streams from the largely peat-covered Millstone Grit country to the north.

EYAM

The high ground to the east of Bradwell Dale, extending southwards to Hucklow Edge and eastwards to Eyam Edge, is composed of Namurian strata lying, probably with unconformity, upon the limestones. These Namurian strata begin at the base with the Edale Shales of variable thickness. The lowest zone with *Cravenoceras leion*, generally not present along the limestone boundary, has been proved in a borehole near Great Hucklow, as well as in another borehole put down in the small Namurian outlier near Wardlow Mires, two and a half kilometres to the south.

The Edale Shales are succeeded by the Mam Tor Beds and Shale Grit which give rise to the variable landscape around Abney, while major sandstones are responsible for Bradwell, Hucklow and Eyam Edges.

To the south of Eyam Edge lies the village of Eyam, a village probably best known in connexion with the Great Plague of 1665. The disease was carried to Eyam in a box of clothes sent from London to a local tailor. At that time the population of Eyam was about 350 and of these all but fifty died in the course of seven months. The disease was contained within the village through the efforts of the rector, William Mompesson.

Eyam was the centre of a prosperous lead-mining area, and indeed today it is closely connected with the only remaining large-scale working of mineral veins in the Peak District; Glebe Mines Ltd produce large quantities of galena, fluor-spar, and barytes each year from mines at Ladywash and Sallet Hole as well as from open works on Longstone Edge. The district is crossed by a plexus of mineral veins; the direction of these veins is variable but many run WSW–ENE. Prior to the era of modern mine pumps, many of the veins had been worked to considerable depths and when pumps failed to lower the water-level it was the practice in the Peak District to de-water by constructing underground drainage tunnels or 'soughs'. Because drainage was generally into one of the rivers of the district a lower limit for the altitude of these soughs was already set. Some of the mineral veins of the Eyam area were extremely rich and in some cases fortunes were made. The Hucklow Edge Vein is one of these; it can be followed for a considerable distance in the limestone country by means of open works and shafts. It disappears beneath a cover of Namurian strata at Eyam Edge, but was worked under this cover from deep shafts of which the Ladywash Mine shaft is one. Some of these shafts are over 300m deep. Most of the mine headstocks have disappeared from the landscape. The steel headgear of the Glebe Mine close to the Eyam village dates from shortly before World War I though the shaft dates from the eighteenth century. As in many of the other formerly prosperous mining areas of the Peak District, open works and hillocks abound; many of the latter have been largely removed or are now being worked for any fluor-spar or galena they may contain. A number of small family businesses are based on working material formerly thrown away as being worthless; they 'tribute' the materials to Glebe Mines Ltd.

The village of Eyam is built on the Eyam Limestones of which a thickness of about forty metres is present. At the top about twelve metres of flat-reef are developed. On the west side of Cucklet Dale small knoll-reefs appear in the Eyam Limestones.

THE EYAM AND WOO DALE BOREHOLES

About a kilometre south of Eyam is Middleton Dale, running E–W and followed by the main road from Peak Forest to Stoney Middleton and Calver. It is a striking dale with lofty cliffs especially on the north side near Stoney Middleton, but the southern side has been spoiled by quarrying. These cliffs provide almost continuous exposures of the D_2 Monsal Dale Beds. At Shining Cliff, where the road to Eyam branches off, there is access to about sixty metres of the lower part of the succession in almost horizontal beds. There are several fossiliferous bands including one with *Lonsdaleia floriformis*, but the most interesting is a coral band about fifty metres above the base of this section which carries *Orionastraea placenta* and so permits of a ready correlation with the section in Bradwell Dale. The Eyam Limestones which are flat-reefs here succeed a potholed surface of the Monsal Dale Beds and extend northwards to disappear beneath the Namurian. Between Shining Cliff and Stoney Middleton dark limestones at the base of the Eyam Limestones form steep grassed and wooded slopes above the cliffs formed by the Monsal Dale Beds.

At Furness Quarry in Middleton Dale about a kilometre south-south-west of Eyam a deep borehole was put down by the British Geological Survey in 1970–2. This borehole reached a final depth of 1,851m and the results, though not yet published in any detail, are remarkable. Boring started in Monsal Dale Limestones of D_2 age, and proved limestones, lavas and thin tuff bands belonging to the D_2 and D_1 zones, limestones partly dolomitised with fossils indicating the S_2 zone, and below these a very thick sequence of shallow-water limestones belonging to the $C_2 S_1$ zone. The base of the Viséan was at a depth of about 1,730m. The borehole continued downwards into dolomites, mudstones with anhydrite nodules and bands, and greenish-grey and red sandstones to a depth of 1,803m; on palaeontological grounds this group of beds is accepted as a thin Tournaisian sequence. This rests with strong unconformity on mudstones and grey silty mudstones with purple staining which are of Ordovician age.

At Woo Dale in the Wye Valley, eleven kilometres to the south-west of Eyam, a borehole showed Viséan $C_2 S_1$ dolomitised limestones resting unconformably upon andesitic volcanic rocks which are of pre-Carboniferous age. They could be Ordovician or Precambrian in age and only radiometric methods will be able to supply an answer.

The findings of the Woo Dale borehole are quite consistent with marine transgression over a relatively stable block or massif, but the very thick and much more complete sequence proved by the Eyam borehole destroys any hypothetical simplciity of such a block. It may well be that the block had very considerable relief. The average gradient of the old basement surface between Woo Dale and Eyam is approximately 1 in 7.

CHAPTER 9

Monsal Dale and Ashford-in-the-Water

One of the most entrancing views in the whole of the Peak District is to be had from the Monsal Head Hotel at Little Longstone. Looking to the west is the deep valley of the River Wye; apart from the incised meanders around Chee Tor, and closer at hand in Water-cum-Jolly Dale, the river has pursued an easterly course for over fifteen kilometres. Over on the right is the impressive White Cliff in rather thickly bedded white-weathering limestones, with the White Cliff Coral Band which can be examined in a small quarry near the old Crossdale Head Mine, on the left side of the road (Castlegate Lane) to Wardlow Mires, climbing the dip-slope to the north of White Cliff. To the left beyond the Monsal Dale viaduct, which formerly carried a busy main-line railway, is Monsal Dale which courses first of all in an almost easterly direction and then swings round the immense rampart of Fin Cop to resume once more the general easterly flow of the River Wye. At Little Longstone the river alters its course through more than a right angle. The reason for this deviation has never yet been satisfactorily explained. Its origin may well date back to an old Triassic erosion surface, where massive escarpments of Namurian sandstones stood much nearer to Monsal Dale than they do today.

THE HOBS HOUSE CORAL BAND

The Wye flows smoothly through Monsal Dale largely through the existence of a number of weirs. From a fairly wide alluvial strip, now occupied by meadows, the hills rise steeply on each bank. The limestones which have been dissected are the Monsal Dale Beds of D_2 age, well bedded generally dark-grey limestones with bedded and nodular chert. These strata can be examined with advantage at Hobs House, an eerie group of tall limestone stacks situated on the left bank of the Wye almost one kilometre to the west of the Monsal Head Hotel, the easiest means of approach being a footpath gained through a stile to the south of the hotel. This path passes high above the western portal of the Headstone Tunnel and runs along the steep wooded slopes which characterise the left bank of the river hereabouts. The limestone stacks of Hobs House (Figure 34, p68) are partly slipped masses of dark-grey limestones with chert. The bedding is conspicuous, the average thickness of the beds being just under a metre. Here the Hobs House Coral Band is readily visible in the lower parts of several of the stacks. The band is about a metre in thickness; in the lower part it is composed of colonies of species of *Lithostrotion*, especially *L. junceum*, and *Syringopora*. The upper part is crowded with large simple corals, mainly clisiophyllids; many of these lie in a prostrate position as though they had been broken off by wave or current action, but a careful examination shows that they actually grew in a recumbent posture, this possibly reflecting the direction of water-current and food-supply.

All the corals in the Hobs House Coral Band are silicified, that is to say the calcium carbonate of the original coralla has been largely replaced by chert. The silicification was probably contemporaneous with the growth of the chert nodules and bands in the associated limestones. Though the mode of formation and date of this general silicification is not known for certain, it seems likely to have occurred shortly after deposition.

Because the corals are silicified and the limestone matrix is not, it is possible to extract the corals by placing them, after removing as much extraneous matrix as possible, in a bath of dilute hydrochloric acid. The insoluble residue other than the corals will be found to contain numerous small brachiopods which were not readily visible to the naked eye on the limestone blocks. Nature has provided such insoluble residues, especially the corals by natural solution over a long period; if the soil over the outcrop of this coral band, or of the White Cliff Coral Band near the Crossdale Head Mine north of the Monsal Head Hotel, is carefully excavated well-preserved silicified corals can be found.

IGNEOUS ROCKS IN MONSAL DALE

A lava flow interbedded with the dark limestones with chert crops out at river-level just to the west of Hobs House, and its outcrop can be traced along the hillside on the left bank of the Wye southwards as far as New Bridge on the main Buxton–Bakewell road which runs through beautiful Taddington Dale. Where Taddington Dale joins Monsal Dale to the north-west of New Bridge, a lower flow of lava crops out as an inlier in the floor of the valley and gives rise to a large area of swampy ground near the river (Figure 59).

It seems possible that these two lava flows are at somewhat higher horizons than the upper and lower lava flows of Miller's Dale as, unlike the latter area, the limestones between the lava flows in Monsal Dale are generally dark-coloured and carry a considerable amount of chert. Moreover, we have seen that the upper lava flow of Miller's Dale dies out eastwards near Litton Mill and a similar extinction of this flow was seen in Taddington Dale, at a point almost due south of Litton Mill, when the Taddington by-pass road was constructed

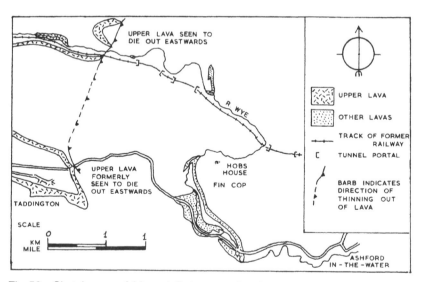

Fig 59 Sketch-map of Monsal Dale area showing likely line of dying out of Miller's Dale Upper Lava

shortly before World War II. In other words, the upper lava flow of Monsal Dale lies to the east of the line along which it can be shown that the Upper Lava of Miller's Dale dies out. It is unfortunate that all these basaltic flows show such lithological similarities in the field that they can not be distinguished, and resort is necessary to the associated limestones. These lavas are almost invariably very altered, and they yield poor thin-sections (Figure 60). It is conceivable that a study of the trace elements in the various lava flows might lead to the discovery of some distinguishing characteristics.

At New Bridge, the upper of the two lavas of Monsal Dale is closely associated with a sill-like intrusion. There is an excellent exposure of this intrusion on the left bank of the river, and on the roadside where about six metres of hard, compact, ophitic olivine dolerite showing spheroidal weathering can be seen. A short distance to the north this sill is seen to rest upon dark limestones with chert, but there is no visible marmorisation of the limestones. In thin-section the dolerite of the sill is seen to be altered, the olivine being replaced by calcite and serpentine, though in some sections the feldspars and augite are quite fresh.

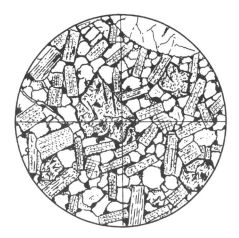

Fig 60   Thin-section of fairly fresh basaltic lava from Monsal Dale. The diameter of the field is about 4mm. The olivine has decomposed to serpentine and iron ore (black) and the feldspars are largely converted to clay degradation products

From New Bridge, the River Wye, having been deflected by the upstanding mass of Fin Cop, with is beautiful dip-slope beyond the summit, resumes its general easterly course. The valley widens somewhat before narrowing again at the peaceful village of Ashford-in-the-Water which lies about three kilometres west-north-west of the market town of Bakewell.

THE ASHFORD MARBLE

Ashford-in-the-Water was for many years the centre of a marble industry, the beds worked being dark-grey limestones of upper D_2 or Brigantian age.

To the geologist, a marble is a rock with a saccharoidal appearance, a limestone which has been recrystallised by metamorphic processes, usually with the elimination of any fossils originally present. Marbles can be of almost any colour though the popular impression is that of a white rock used for statuary purposes, such as the Carrara marble from the Apuan Alps in northern Italy. Marbles are also very variable in composition, for the latter depends upon the chemical composition of the limestone prior to metamorphism. For example, a dolomitic limestone when thermally metamorphosed would produce a marble which contains the mineral brucite as well as calcite, and would be called a brucite marble.

There are several examples of genuine marbles in the Peak District, all of them produced by thermal metamorphism of beds of the Carboniferous Limestone by basaltic intrusions. Such can be seen in Tideswell Dale to the south of Tideswell, in Great Rocks Dale to the north-west of the Chee Tor where the white Chee Tor Limestones have been intensely marmorised by a complex of intrusions which might well have served as feeders for some of the lava flows, and at Peak Forest ten kilometres north-east of Buxton where the Peak Forest Sill has a similar effect.

However, these occurrences of true marble are too small to have attracted attention with a view to working them.

The Ashford Black Marble is not a true marble according to our definition. It is a dark-grey limestone containing a considerable amount of argillaceous and carbonaceous material and which takes a high polish. When polished the rock appears to be almost black and frequently shows small fragments of crinoid columnals.

The marble was worked in the hills around Kirk Dale to the west of Ashford-in-the-Water certainly as early as the sixteenth century. During Victorian times particularly it was used for table-tops, washstand tops, ornamental vases, clock-cases, and jewellery, and was employed in churches for floors and statuary pieces. This marble was frequently inlaid with other Peak District limestones, often fossiliferous ones, and this gave rise to an industry which flourished almost to the outbreak of World War I. About this time, black 'marbles' were also worked for similar purposes in Devonshire, at Kilkenny in Ireland, and at Poolvash in the Isle of Man. However, Ashford seems to have been almost alone in producing inlaid work, and pieces can still be seen in some Peak District homes today.

The Ashford marble occurs in well-defined beds generally about half a metre in thickness. There is somewhat lenticular and nodular chert associated with the beds and careful selection must have been necessary. The marble was worked north of the River Wye west of Ashford village in the Rookery Plantation where old workings can be seen; south of the river a great amount of marble was extracted both by quarrying and by mining in the hill called the Arrock, in Kirkdale and in Nettler Dale. Some of the old underground workings can still be entered.

Limestones with shaly partings slightly above those worked for marble in the past can be examined behind the footpath on the south side of the Ashford by-pass road. These dark-grey limestones with some chert are at about the same horizon as those exposed in the Headstone cutting east of Little Longstone (p 70). They contain some well-preserved brachiopods and occasional fragmentary trilobites. They dip in a south-easterly direction at a low angle, and are succeeded by the Namurian Edale Shales.

CHAPTER 10

Matlock, the Via Gellia and Brassington

Below Ashford-in-the-Water the River Wye flows in a south-easterly direction following very approximately the junction between the Dinantian limestones and the Namurian shales and sandstones. The regional dip is low and generally towards the east, although there are some deviations as several subsidiary anticlines and synclines ripple the eastern limb of the main structure. For the most part the Wye has excavated a fairly wide valley in Namurian strata from Bakewell, past Haddon Hall where the combined waters from Bradford Dale and Lathkill Dale join it from the south-west, to Great Rowsley where the Wye joins the River Derwent coming from the north. The Derwent continues to flow in a southerly direction. At Darley Dale, midway between Great Rowlsey and Matlock, the alluvial plain of the Derwent exceeds a kilometre in width. On the right bank the limestone ground rises towards Winster, the centre of a once prosperous lead-mining industry. On the left bank the rising ground beyond the edge of the flood-plain consists of the shales and sandstones of the Namurian.

At Matlock the valley of the Derwent suddenly narrows to a gorge as the river becomes entrenched in the limestones, and this gorge continues through Matlock Bath to Cromford, a distance of about five kilometres, before a wide flood-plain is again developed. Matlock Dale, as the gorge is called, carries the main road and also the railway, the latter being carried through a tunnel beneath High Tor, a precipitous cliff of limestone over 100m in height between Matlock and Matlock Bath (Figure 61). It seems likely that the presence of thermal springs led to baths being built here by the Romans, for masonry, reputed to be Roman, has been found during excavations at Matlock Bath. The waters of these thermal springs, which have a constant temperature of 20°C, first seem to have attracted attention

114

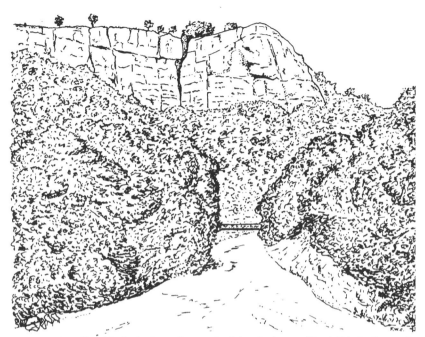

Fig 61   High Tor, Matlock, from the north. A lenticular reef is visible in the main face

in more recent times in the seventeenth century, and during the latter half of the last century the baths became increasingly popular for their curative properties.

The discovery near Matlock of several pigs of lead with Roman inscriptions lends credence to the view that the Romans worked lead mines in the area. On the Heights of Abraham to the west of Matlock Dale there are many old lead-mines and several caverns. In the Rutland Cavern, the largest of the caverns in this district, there is a gallery called the Roman Hall in which there are traces of Roman handicraft dating back almost two thousand years to the time when the Romans worked lead ore here. Nearby is the Masson Cavern, part of which is also thought to have been a Roman lead-mine. Some years ago when miners were following a vein of galena they broke into a large natural cavern roughly 70m long, 30m high, and up to 15m wide.

In various parts of Matlock Dale, but especially on the lower slopes of the Heights of Abraham to the south of Matlock Bath there are deposits of calcareous tufa, which has been precipitated from spring-waters carrying calcium bicarbonate in solution. There are several so-called petrifying springs in Matlock Bath. It was fashionable some years ago to immerse all manner of objects in the pool below a spring and to leave them there for some years. When taken out, an old top hat might have been found to be exceedingly heavy and was described as having been 'turned into stone', that is petrified. In fact, the hat was unchanged inside a coating of calcium carbonate, stalagmite or tufa.

The Cumberland Cavern at Matlock Bath is also extensive. A well known guide-book published since World War II, in referring to this cavern, states 'The cavern is geologically of interest as exhibiting the dislocations of strata and other effects of that mighty volcanic force which upheaved these grand hills.' This is an example of the way in which outmoded cataclysmic ideas are perpetuated.

From the main road from Darley Dale to Matlock where the road and railway closely approach the river a large quarry is seen alongside the road from Matlock to Snitterton. This is Cawdor Quarry and it shows the succession in the upper part of the Dinantian. The Upper Lava of the Matlock area is seen to be succeeded by about thirty metres of thickly bedded light-grey limestones with typical D_2 fossils including the coral *Lonsdaleia floriformis*. These beds have been called the Upper Lathkill Limestones from their occurrence in Lathkill Dale to the north west. They are similar to the higher D_2 limestones of the Wye Valley section (p 67). Resting unconformably on these beds are dark-grey and grey irregularly bedded limestones which are seen to pass laterally into thinly bedded limestones and shales. There is a rich brachiopod fauna including *Spirifer striatus* (Martin) and *Pugilis pugilis* (Phillips), but the most exciting occurrence is that of the goniatite *Goniatites granosum* Portlock in a thin bed of limestone. This enables a correlation of this group of dark limestones and shales, the Cawdor Limestones, with the P_2 zone of the goniatite-bivalve facies (of basin type), and so with the thin limestones and shales in the Headstone cutting in the Wye Valley section (p 71).

To the north of Cawdor Quarry the basal beds of the Namurian succeed the Cawdor Limestones. They are shales, but in the rising ground to the north of the main road these shales are quickly succeeded by a massive sandstone, the Ashover Grit or Sandstone which, from the marine band above it containing *Reticuloceras superbilingue*, is to be correlated with the Roaches Grit or Sandstone of the Goyt Trough area (p 79). It was in this area that Whitehurst, over 150 years ago, first used the term 'Millstone Grit' for a coarse sharp sandstone, probably the Ashover Sandstone.

At High Tor, the impressive cliff about 130m in height on the left bank of the Derwent between Matlock and Matlock Bath, the Cawdor Limestones, which vary so rapidly, are almost entirely calcareous and include a mass of reef over thirty metres in thickness. This can be seen quite clearly from the main road. These limestones continue southwards to Cromford where the river bends sharply to the east. All along the valley from Matlock Bridge to Cromford the Cawdor Limestones of P_2 age are succeeded by Namurian shales dipping gently eastwards. The steepening slopes above these shales to the east of the Derwent are produced by the more resistant Ashover Sandstone, and it is upon the outcrop of this sandstone that Riber Castle is situated. The well known local beauty-spot, Black Rocks, on the north-west flank of Cromford Moor just over a kilometre south of Cromford village, is also in the Ashover Sandstone outcrop; the important Bonsall Fault, the master fault of the Matlock district which strikes roughly NW–SE, passes through Cromford and displaces the sandstone outcrop.

The Bonsall Fault has been traced from Cromford north-west almost to Arbor Low, the ancient stone circle on Middleton Common, a distance of about sixteen kilometres. The average throw of the fault is about 100m to the south, and the fault does not appear to be mineralised. This major fault separates areas of different fundamental structure. On the north side of the fault the limestones dip into the Stanton Syncline, one of a number of subsidiary folds on the eastern limb of the main anticline of the Peak District, and are similarly gently folded in the country to the north of Cromford. On the south side, the limestones are not folded in this way but are broken into fault blocks which are tilted at different angles.

The village of Cromford, where Richard Arkwright the inventor of the spinning jenny set up the first cotton mill on the River Derwent, is situated at the south end of Matlock Dale. It is reached by turning right off the Derby road in the direction of Wirksworth, the former centre of a thriving lead-mining industry. For the Via Gellia one turns right again after proceeding 350m, and reaches the Pig of Lead Inn after another kilometre. At the inn the road forks right for Bonsall and left for the Via Gellia.

The Via Gellia is not, as its name might suggest, a Roman road. It is the latinised name of a drive built by John Gell of Hopton Hall near Carsington, and is now used as the name of the steep-sided wooded valley running westwards from Cromford to Hopton Wood where the road from Wirksworth enters from the south-east. Beyond Hopton Wood the valley is known as the Griffe Grange Valley, and this opens out to the west at Grangemill. Limestones of D_1 age are exposed along the wooded slopes either naturally or through quarrying. Indeed, the splendour of the Via Gellia is greatly diminished at the Cromford end by quarries and their associated plant.

Beginning at Cromford, the junction between the Cawdor Limestones of P_2 age with the underlying thickly-bedded light-grey limestones of D_2 age (which have been called the Upper Lathkill Limestones), is exposed behind a building on the side of the road south of the mill pond at Cromford. The Bonsall Fault, the general delineation of which has already been described, can be seen in section in the cliff at the Cromford garage, and its position is also clear in the road near the centre of Bonsall village.

The Lathkill Limestones rest upon a thin lava flow which can be traced high up on both sides of the Via Gellia. Below this lava flow the Via Gellia Limestones crop out; they are thickly bedded or massive light-grey limestones, sometimes highly crinoidal rocks, which include some darker-grey beds in the upper part. About one kilometre to the west of the Pig of Lead Inn, and on the north side of the Via Gellia, one of these darker-grey beds is exposed. It yields corals and brachiopods typical of the D_1 zone such as *Palaeosmilia murchisoni* (Edwards and Haime) and *Davidsonina septosa*. The presence of the latter together with the general lithology of the bed, and its hummocky upper surface, strongly suggests correlation with the *D. septosa* band of the Wye Valley section (p 47), in which case the Via Gellia lava flow must be at about the same horizon as the Lower Lava of Miller's Dale. It is known that there are more than two volcanic horizons in the Miller's Dale area, and there are also several in the Matlock district, but it has been argued for a very long time that there is probably no correlation of volcanic episodes as between the two districts. The presence of the *D. septosa* band in the Via Gellia is therefore of importance in this connexion.

Certain beds in the Via Gellia Limestones have been quarried for many years for use as 'marble'. The largest and best-known quarries are those of Hoptonwood about 600m south of the junction of the

Fig 62   Crinoidal limestone from Hopton Wood, Derbyshire; portion of polished surface. Half natural size

Wirksworth road with the Via Gellia. These beds are thickly bedded or massive light-grey to oatmeal-coloured limestones, frequently highly crinoidal. The limestones take a high polish and are much used for indoor cappings and stone facings (Figure 62). The *Davidsonina septosa* band fauna occurs in Hoptonwood Quarry.

The D_1 zone Via Gellia Limestones have a maximum thickness of about 150m. Below them are dark limestones with *Daviesiella llangollensis* proving the presence of the Holkerian stage.

Proceeding westwards into the Griffe Grange Valley the D_1 limestones are patchily exposed. On the north side of this valley is the village of Ible. Just west of Griffe Grange a footpath leads up a small ravine to the village. As the path passes northwards out of the wood pieces of dolerite are to be seen. These and other outcrops mark the outcrop of the Ible Sill. This intrusion consists of an ophitic dolerite with conspicuous olivine phenocrysts. The outcrop of the sill is quadrilateral in shape and measures 800m from east to west and about 600m from north to south. Its southern boundary closely approaches the road through the Griffe Grange Valley.

THE GRANGEMILL VENTS

To the north-west of Ible is the hamlet of Grangemill, which has interested geologists for nearly a hundred years on account of the existence of two volcanic necks or vents. They appear as two dome-shaped hills with steep grassy slopes and stand in marked contrast to the limestone scenery all around. The larger of the two vents is elliptical in shape and its outcrop stretches northwards from the cross-roads at Grangemill for about 600m. The smaller vent lies immediately to the north of the larger and is mainly on the east side of the Grangemill–Winster road. Exposures of the rocks in the vents are now poor, but scattered blocks are of an agglomerate of lapilli in a cement of fine volcanic detritus, a certain amount of interstitial calcite, and fragments of marmorised limestone.

These vents mark the positions of small volcanoes which spattered or poured their products into the Dinantian seas. It has not been established that they gave rise to any of the major lava flows of the area. Indeed, the latter may well have been fed from submarine fissure eruptions.

LEAD MINING IN THE PEAK DISTRICT

The area around Matlock, Wirksworth, Brassington, Youlgreave and Winster is riddled with old lead-mines which have exploited the mainly vertical mineral-veins known as rakes (Figure 63). Some of these rakes represent mineralisation along faults possibly in late Carboniferous times; others seem to be mineral infillings of fissures opened under tensional stress with post-mineralisation shearing to account for the horizontal slickensides along the limestone/vein interface. The main gangue minerals in this area are calcite, fluorite and some barytes.

Mining in this part of the Peak District probably dates back to Roman times, for several pigs of lead bearing Roman inscriptions

Fig 63 Open-worked section of the Long Rake to the west of Youlgreave. A cross-cutting calcite vein is exposed and the limestone walls of the main rake show horizontal slickensides

have been found, notably at Matlock Bank, Tansley Moor and Cromford Nether Moor. The Peak District pigs of lead bear inscriptions such as LVT and LVTVD from which the owner and place of manufacture can be surmised. These inscriptions may indicate an old Roman settlement called Lutadarum which is thought to have been situated in the Matlock, Winster and Wirksworth area, though there is no proof of this. None of these crude ingots bears a date but there is reason to believe that the one found on Cromford Nether Moor was made in the period AD 117–38. Possibly mineral veins were first discovered during ploughing of fields, and this could have led to many of them being worked opencast. It seems likely that the Romans did work some of the veins by mining, as on Masson Hill, Matlock.

The regulations, customs and rights in connexion with the working of lead ores in the Peak District are both ancient and quaint. They were probably first enunciated in the Wirksworth district and some of them are practised today. There is a very considerable literature concerned with these ancient leadmining laws, some of which date back to 1288 in which year Edward I decreed that an inquisition to investigate claims by lead-miners should be held at Ashbourne.

Under the various provisions, a newly discovered vein had to be notified to the Barmaster at Wirksworth. After registration by the Barmaster and the payment of the first duties in kind, the finders or applicants were permitted to mine the ore under special conditions concerning area of ground, royalties to the landowner or the Crown (usually in kind), and the disposal of waste. Once permission to work had been granted, the owner of the ground, who would generally draw the royalties, was required to allow access to the site and an area of ground for the disposal of waste.

Barmoot Courts were held fairly frequently from the beginning of the seventeenth century in order to deal with squabbles over ownership of part of a vein, non-payment of royalties or other debts incurred in mining, and the valuation of deposits. The Court consisted of the Barmaster, and owners and others possessing expertise in mining who served as a jury during the hearings of a case.

With the demise of lead-mining in the Peak District the Barmoot Court, although it is still maintained in traditional fashion, has ceased to operate in this way. Nevertheless, even today, the chance discovery of a vein carrying galena during the quarrying of limestone must be reported to the Barmaster who, in all probability, will pay an official visit to the site. These ancient mining-laws probably had their beginnings in Saxon times; they were codified at the Ashbourne Inquisition of 1288, and after inevitable revision and modification were finally embodied in Acts of Parliament of 1851 and 1852.

The life of the lead-miner in the Peak District was uncomfortable, hard, and usually poorly paid. Before the advent of explosives for blasting underground, primitive methods of shattering limestone and vein material were employed. One method consisted in lighting a fire against the working face; by law the fire could not be lighted before four o'clock in the afternoon, and after it had burned all night the heated rock-face was quenched with water. The expansion by heating and rapid contraction by quenching resulted in some shattering.

Miners entered and left the workings by means of rungs fixed into the shaft walls, or sometimes by ladder, often through heights of several hundred metres. The heavy ore was manhandled on sledges or primitive tubs over long distances. Water was a constant source of trouble, and immense energy was expended in the construction of tunnels or soughs through solid limestone in order to drain the water to the nearest river. The earliest soughs date from the seventeenth century, by which time the majority of highly productive mineral-veins had been worked out to the level of the water-table, so that it was impossible to work any lower without some device to lower the water-table. Some of the soughs are several kilometres in length and immense amounts of water can be seen coming from their outlets or 'tails'. There is a sough tail behind some houses in the market square at Cromford, and others are to be seen near the Mill Close Mine on the right bank of the Derwent north-west of Darleybridge. The Mill Close Mine was, until its closure in 1939, one of the most fruitful lead-mines in the world, having raised almost 500,000 tons of galena, and during its productive life it posed some difficult de-watering problems for the mine engineers. In this mine the main galena mineralisation occurs as layers parallel to the stratal dip ('flats') beneath several lava flows.

DOLOMITISATION OF LIMESTONES

The country to the west of Wirksworth and Winster as far as the Ashbourne–Leek road, which largely follows the line of a Roman road, is typical limestone upland lying generally about 350m above sea-level. The altitude ascends above this particularly around Aleck Low near Friden, and below it in the dales which are frequently dry valleys. The area is somewhat bleak and given over largely to rough pasture. Around the scattered farms are arable fields, and the landscape is dotted with small geometrically shaped plantations, predominantly of beech, which sometimes follow the lines of old opencast workings of mineral veins. In various parts of this piece of country the limestones are strongly dolomitised; this applies especially to the district around Brassington, and massive exposures of these dolomites are particularly well seen at Harboro Rocks just over one kilometre north-east of Brassington, on Carsington Pastures, Ballidon Moor and at Rainster Rocks. The cause of the intense dolomitisation is problematical; the main suggestions have been that the dolomite was formed beneath the Dinantian sea, or in Permian times when the region must again have been covered by the sea. The second explanation seems to be the more likely, but unfortunately in this part of the Peak District there are no known deposits younger than those of Carboniferous age which can be used to narrow down the dating of the dolomitisation. The Permo-Triassic rocks have long been stripped from the Peak District surface and the southerly-migrating northern edge of their outcrop now lies well to the south in the latitude of Kedleston and Ashbourne.

TERTIARY POCKET DEPOSITS

Until recent years the Tertiary age of certain peculiar deposits of clays, sands, and gravels in the Peak District had not been established. In the belt of country running north-westwards from

Carsington Pastures, through Friden to Parsley Hay and beyond, these deposits, which have been worked since the beginning of the century, are found filling large pits and hollows in the limestone surface. Some of the pits are very deep, one at Washmere near Friden having been worked to a depth of about fifty metres; others like the ones on Carsington Pastures are shallow. In some the limestone walls are vertical while in others they are sloping. The areas of outcrop of these 'pocket deposits' are wide-ranging; there is one at Friden showing an outcrop area of more than four hectares.

At least sixty pits have been or are being worked and probably many more remain to be discovered. They all occur on the limestone surface having an altitude of 330–360 m above sea-level.

The material infilling a pit frequently shows signs of bedding, but the latter is often greatly disturbed and may approach the vertical (Figure 64). Occasionally, as at Friden, two or more pits are confluent with one another.

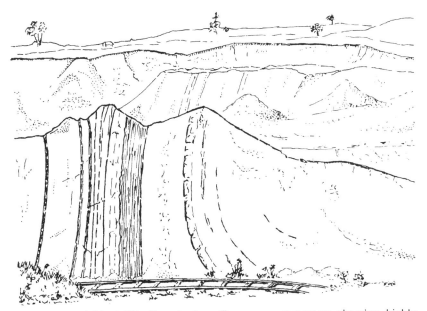

Fig 64 Bees' Nest Pit, Brassington. Temporary exposure showing highly disturbed beds of sands, gravels, and clays

The origin and age of these infilled pits is a problem; it is only recently that some of the deposits have been dated by their fossil contents, and their origin remains a mystery. The actual hollows in the limestone surface appear to be solution-subsidence phenomena, and the subsidence of materials deposited on the limestone surface would account for the disturbed nature of the infilling of solution hollows.

It has been known for some years that blocks of Namurian shale containing goniatites are associated with the sand and gravel deposits. Various ages have been suggested; Permian, Triassic, Rhaetic, Jurassic, Tertiary, and Pleistocene, but no strong evidence has been produced in favour of any one of these until recently.

Some individual beds of the infilling deposits can be traced laterally for some distance. The exposures are ephemeral, for working of the deposits proceeds apace; there is considerable slipping especially after heavy rains, and worked-out parts of pits are used for the tipping of waste. At present, the best exposures are at Bees' Nest Pit and Kirkham' Pit in the Brassington area, and at Kenslow Top Pit near Friden. From exposures in these pits it has been possible to distinguish three main groups of beds. At the base, and resting unconformably on lilac-coloured weathered shales representing the pre-subsidence surface, are sands and gravels in which no fossils have been recognised. These are succeeded by unfossiliferous mottled red and green clays which are succeeded conformably by grey clays with plant remains. These three groups are called the Brassington Formation.

The youngest group, the grey clays, contain fossil plants indicating an Upper Miocene–Lower Pliocene age. The Brassington Formation represents a single cycle of sedimentation in a terrestrial environment, piedmont or river-borne sands and gravels passing up into a lacustrine phase, ending with semi-paludal sediments containing fragments of fossil wood and thin pieces of lignite.

All the evidence suggests that in late Miocene-early Pliocene times this deposition took place on a Namurian shale cover to the limestone, and that the only remnants of the deposits are those which subsided into solution hollows in the limestone. It is thought that the total amount of subsidence is of the order of 150–250m, which would mean that the Lower Pliocene land surface of the Peak District approached an altitude of 450m above sea-level. A great deal of material has, of course, been removed from the area since early Pliocene times when the Brassington Formation was laid down, and this has lowered the surface. Acting, however, in the opposite direction since the Alpine folding, there has been a slow but steady uplift of the Peak District in common with the rest of upland Britain. This uplift which continues today is no doubt responsible for the rejuvenation of streams and rivers which have incised their courses producing the typical dales and valleys of the Peak District (Figure 65).

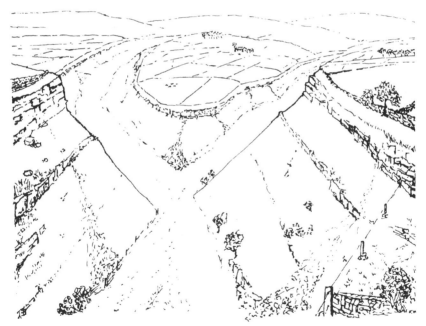

Fig 65 A typical dry valley. Looking southwards in Deep Dale into Back Dale on the right and Horseshoe Dale on the left. Hills in Chee Tor Limestones in the distance

CHAPTER 11

Ashover

At Matlock, the boundary between the Viséan limestones and the shales and sandstones of the Namurian corresponds very approximately with the course of the River Derwent. The initial slopes in the ascent to Riber Castle are of shales masked largely by solifluxion deposits frequently termed 'head'. The dip is low and in a north-easterly direction. Shortly before Riber Castle is reached the thick Ashover Grit or Sandstone succeeds the shales and forms a feature. The castle is built on this sandstone (Figure 66).

Continuing north-eastwards from Riber Castle the general structure for the next five kilometres is gently synclinal, and on Tansley Moor the Ashover Sandstone is succeeded by shales which in turn are covered by the next higher sandstone, the Chatsworth Grit or Sandstone. This sandstone forms a belt of high moorland country stretching to the north-west of Tansley Moor and high above the

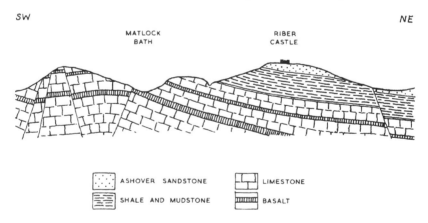

Fig 66 Sketch-section through Matlock Bath and Riber Castle. Length about 8km. Vertical scale exaggerated about four times

128

valley of the Derwent. To the east of Tansley Moor the axis of the shallow syncline has been crossed and the beds now dip gently westwards. The eastern edge of the Ashover Sandstone forms a marked escarpment facing north-eastwards.

Just over six kilometres north-east of Matlock this escarpment overlooks the verdant valley of the River Amber which, formed by the junction of two small streams some five kilometres to the north, flows southwards to join the Derwent. Lying secluded in the valley is the typical Pennine village of Ashover. For some distance the River Amber roughly follows the axis of the Ashover Anticline which, running in a NW–SE direction, brings the Dinantian rocks, limestones, shales, and volcanic rocks to the surface. This is the Ashover Inlier which is due to the combination of a river valley and a subsidiary anticline. The Namurian rocks, shales and thick sandstones form a marked rim to this inlier. On the eastern side the dip of the Namurian strata, as in the vicinity of Alton, is steeper than on the western limb. This dip persists to the east so that the outcrop of the Namurian is less than a kilometre in width to the east of Ashover, and the Derbyshire coalfield is reached. In fact the coal-mining town of Clay Cross lies only seven kilometres to the north-east of Ashover.

DINANTIAN ROCKS OF ASHOVER

The inlier of Ashover and a fault-terminated inlier at Crich nine kilometres to the south provide the most easterly exposures of Dinantian rocks. To the east, the latter are rapidly covered by later Carboniferous rocks which in turn are succeeded unconformably by the Permian and Triassic rocks.

For our purposes, Ashover may be said to lie on the eastern edge of the Peak District.

The valley of the River Amber around Ashover is relatively quiet as it is off the beaten track, the nearest main road being that between Matlock and Chesterfield which lies over a kilometre north-west of the village at Kelstedge.

The main occupation of the district is farming, although until the outbreak of World War II quarrying was probably of greater importance. Some quarrying of limestone still goes on, but the working of the local Namurian sandstones for masonry, kerbs, and setts, and for the production of pulp-stones used in the paper industry, has ceased.

The limestone inlier measures roughly two kilometres from NW–SE along the anticlinal axis and about one kilometre at right angles to this. The outcrop is approximately oval in shape with the valley of the Amber following the major axis, and Ashover is situated in the north-east of the inlier.

The oldest rocks exposed in the inlier are dark-green frequently laminated tuffs. These may be seen in various abandoned quarries particularly in the Fall Hill and Hockley quarries on the east side of the road running southwards from Ashover along the left bank of the River Amber. The best exposure is undoubtedly at Hockley Quarry where a cutting leads into the quarry from the main road. This cutting shows ten metres of green bedded tuffs, with lapilli and fragments of limestone and chert, overlain unconformably by thickly bedded light-grey limestones with scattered fossils of D_2 age.

The base of the tuff is nowhere exposed and it is difficult to assess the thickness of the tuff from surface evidence alone. At Fall Hill Quarry a shaft was sunk entirely in igneous rocks to a depth of seventy metres. In a borehole put down by the British Geological Survey at Fallgate, alongside the river at the southern end of the inlier, a thickness of about 106m of tuff was recorded. The tuff in the cores was dark-green, grey and purple and contained pieces of pumice. The lower contact of the tuffs with older limestones was abrupt and irregular, and the borehole reached a depth of about 250m proving olivine basalt lavas with some intercalated limestones, and some volcanic breccias. This is an extraordinarily thick sequence of Lower Carboniferous volcanic rocks recorded here, in the core of the Ashover Anticline. These volcanic rocks comprise a complex of lava flows and volcanic breccias succeeded by the laminated tuffs. It may well be that they mark the site of a volcanic centre in Lower Carboniferous times when the Ashover Anticline had already been marked out or initiated.

The Viséan limestones above the tuffs are well exposed at Milltown

Quarry, at Hockley Quarry a little to the south-east of the Red Lion Hotel, Ashover, and in the old quarries at Fall Hill. Higher beds are exposed on both banks of the Amber close to where it enters the limestone inlier, particularly at Butts Quarry, and also in the old quarry in Stars Wood at the southern end of the inlier. The lower limestones are generally thickly bedded or massive and light-grey in colour; the upper beds are thinner, darker and contain more chert than the lower.

The total thickness of the limestone above the tuffs in the core of the anticline has been estimated at about seventy metres. This has been confirmed in a borehole put down in 1955 by the British Geological Survey at Highoredish about three kilometres SSE of Ashover, though it was somewhat thinner in another borehole 800m east of Tansley.

The thickly bedded limestones yield numerous productids such as *Productus concinnus, P.* cf. *maximus,* and corals including *Lithostrotion junceum, Lonsdaleia floriformis* (Martin) and *Palaeosmilia regia* (Phillips). These indicate a D₂ horizon. Certain other fossils which have been recorded such as *Spirifer striatus* (Martin), *Pseudammusium* sp., *Schizophoria* sp. and *Dielasma hastata* (J. de C. Sowerby) are more commonly associated with the reef facies than with the massif facies in the Peak District, and may indicate that the edge of the massif lay not far from Ashover.

The higher beds of the Viséan consisting of thinly bedded dark-grey limestones with chert and intercalated shales and mudstones with *Posidonia corrugata* (Etheridge), *Neoglyphioceras georgiensis* (Miller and Furnish) are probably to be referred to the P₂ zone.

NAMURIAN ROCKS OF ASHOVER

The beds immediately above the limestones are shales which are not well exposed owing to deposits of head, but shales with *Reticuloceras* sp. are exposed in the bed and banks of Marsh Brook north-west of Butts at the northern edge of the limestone inlier, and on the fossil evidence these shales are of Namurian age. These shales are succeeded by the Ashover Sandstone or Grit which forms a marked feature running around the inlier. This feature is particularly strong on the western limb of the anticline, and the outcrop is marked by a series of abandoned quarries, Cocking Tor, Bradley Tor, and Ambervale quarries. On the eastern limb of the anticline the outcrop of the sandstone is also easy to follow, but it is narrower than on the western limb owing to the somewhat higher dip.

At Knotcross Farm south of Ashover Hay the western and eastern outcrops of the Ashover Sandstone approach one another within about 500m owing to the slight southerly plunge of the fold.

In order to elucidate the sequence in detail, the Institute of Geological Sciences put down borings, in 1955, at Uppertown just over three kilometres north-west of Ashover, at Fallgate alongside the River Amber at the southern limit of the limestone inlier, at Highoredish on Carr Brook about two kilometres south-south-east of Ashover, and at a point about 800m east of Tansley. All except the Fallgate borehole began in the *Reticuloceras bilingue* (R_2) zone of the Namurian and went down through the underlying Namurian beds and into the Viséan limestones. Marine bands identifying the R_1, H, E_2, and E_1 zones were proved, and in the E_1 zone *Cravenoceras leion* marked the base of the Namurian. The boreholes afford no evidence of a physical break between the basal Namurian and the highest Viséan (P_2, Cawdor Limestones) nor is there any reason to suspect the presence of any but a minor gap in the fossil sequence. This conformable sequence contrasts sharply with the major break between the Namurian and the Viséan on the western and northern margins of the limestone terrain of the Peak District.

As compared with other parts of the Peak District, that part of the Namurian succession below the *Reticuloceras bilingue* marine band is very thin. This is due in part to the absence of the Kinder Scout Grit, Shale Grit and other sandstones present in the Kinder Scout–Edale district from Ashover, but the mudstones have also become thinner. For example, 270m of sandstones, shales and 'crowstones' of E_1 age at Gun Hill thirty-five kilometres west of Ashover are represented by under eleven metres of mudstones at Ashover.

The Ashover Inlier is heavily mineralised mostly by rakes running in an E–W direction. The main minerals are galena, sphalerite, fluorite, calcite, and barytes. A great deal of galena has been removed and spoil-heaps around some of the abandoned mines still yield hand-specimens of minerals. The mineral veins beneath the Namurian ground between Ashover Inlier and Matlock have not been extensively worked, and large reserves probably exist in this area.

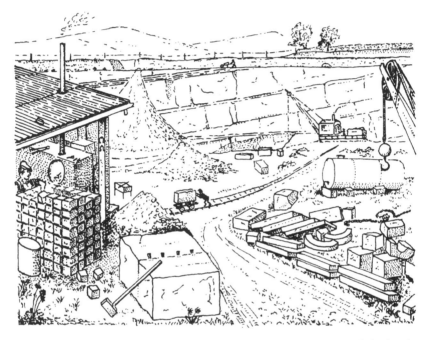

A sandstone quarry in the Peak District producing setts and kerbs for roadmaking and a certain amount of masonry stone. This kind of scene was commonplace on the Namurian and Coal Measure sandstones around the Peak District before World War II, and is the author's impression drawn from memory

CHAPTER 12

The Valley of the River Dove

The main watershed of the southern Pennines lies along Axe Edge, a marked feature formed by thick Namurian sandstones, to the south of Buxton (p 78). Streams rising on the western side of this edge coalesce to form rivers which run into the Irish Sea. On the eastern side the drainage is by a long and circuitous route into the North Sea by way of the R. Trent and the Humber. One of the important rivers rising on Axe Edge is the Dove. It arises in a spring at Dove Head on the Buxton–Leek road and, flowing in a general south-easterly direction, forms the county boundary between Derbyshire and Staffordshire for a distance of nearly ninety kilometres before joining the River Trent to the north-east of Burton-on-Trent. For the first seven kilometres or so the Dove runs into a shallow valley cut into Namurian shales and subsidiary sandstones which show rapid changes of dip probably owing to collapse into solution cavities in the underlying Viséan limestones.

From Hollinsclough, the River Dove flows to the south of the extraordinary reef limestone eminences, Chrome Hill and Parkhouse Hill, and as far as Hartington its course coincides roughly with the shale-limestone boundary. To the south-west of Hartington the river has become entrenched in the limestone, first in the impressive gorge of Beresford Dale (once the home of Charles Cotton), then into Wolfscote Dale between Wolfscote Hill and Gratton Hill, and finally through Mill Dale into Dove Dale before proceeding southwards to enter the Triassic country near Ashbourne.

Dove Dale is a narrow gorge-like valley some five kilometres in length between the hamlets of Milldale and Ilam where the River Manifold enters as a tributary to the River Dove from the north-west. This part of the valley of the Dove, popularly associated with the name of Izaak Walton, the author of *The Compleat Angler,* is one of the

134

scenic gems not only of the Peak District but of Britain. A wide variety of erosional features in limestones, cliffs, tors, a natural arch and caves along the valley entrenched between high limestone hills, are partly clothed with a variety of vegetation, and these combine with a river sometimes smooth, sometimes tumultuous to produce an ever-changing scene.

Generally speaking it is better to ascend than to descend in exploring the scenery of a valley, but it pays to make the return journey in Dove Dale. Cars can be parked in a public car-park on the right bank of the river opposite the Izaak Walton Hotel at Ilam. Thorpe Cloud rises up on the left bank and is referred to later. There is a footpath through the dale to Milldale, a distance of five kilometres, which is passable throughout its length except after very heavy rains when the section in the narrowest part of the valley, the straits to the north of Reynard's Cave, may be flooded.

The geology of the valley of the Dove is rather complex in that part which cuts through the Carboniferous Limestone. In the first place all three facies are represented; generally thickly bedded almost unfolded limestones of the shelf or rigid block environment, thick virtually non-bedded reef limestones of the areas marginal to the block, and rather thinly bedded dark limestones and shaly beds, often highly folded, which belong to the basin facies. Each facies gives rise to particular scenic features, but generally speaking the most spectacular in Dove Dale are the cliffs, tors and caves in the thick reef limestones. To add to the complexity associated with the facies variations the rocks are gently folded roughly along NNW–SSE; axes; a broad anticline with minor folds on its limbs has an axis approximately following the course of the River Dove. There are several faults affecting the ground to the east of Dove Dale.

Considerable difficulty attends correlations of the three limestone facies and as only a few horizons in all can be equated with any degree of certainty on palaeontological grounds, local names have been introduced for the different formations (Appendix VII).

A geological traverse is best started from Hartington, the picturesque Derbyshire village grouped around a green, which is a popular centre for tourists and for sheep- and cattle-farmers. Taking the road opposite the church, follow the lane through a sharp left-hand bend and turn right along the lane to Beresford Dale. This lane going southwards passes over the Alsop Moor Limestones which show scattered exposures on Wolfscote Hill to the east. These limestones have a thickness of about 300m; they are fairly thickly bedded, light-grey in colour and poorly fossiliferous. The D_1 zone fossil *Dibunophyllum bourtonense* may be found in places, and on this basis these limestones are regarded as massif facies of D_1 age, the approximate equivalents of the Chee Tor Limestones of the Wye Valley (p 48). All around Wolfscote Hill there are bedded limestone breccias apparently about sixty-five metres above the base of the Alsop Moor Limestones, and there is a good exposure of them in the field to the north of Frank's Rock just above the incised Wolfscote Dale. The dale itself is excavated in reef limestones to which the name Narrowdale Limestone has been given; these are unbedded light-grey limestones with layers of reef-tufa, shell beds and local limestone breccias. The fauna includes the massif D_1 zone fossil *Palaeosmilia murchisoni* (Edwards and Haime) and the goniatite *Beyrichoceras castletonense* which denotes the B_2 zone. Clearly in Wolfscote Dale we are very close to the western edge of the massif in D_1 times, and the Alsop Moor Limestones pass laterally into the Narrowdale Limestone.

Narrowdale Hill lies just over one kilometre to the south-west of Frank's Rock; the B_2 reef limestones of this hill have yielded many

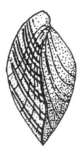

Fig 67 *Dielasma hastata* from the Lower Carboniferous reef limestones of Narrowdale Hill, Staffordshire. Lateral view to show colour banding preserved on pedicle valve. Natural size

beautiful specimens, particularly of brachiopods, preserved in museum collections. On some specimens there are traces of the original colour-banding (Figure 67).

The country immediately to the west of Beresford Dale is underlain by Namurian shales. A slight eastward projection of their outcrop brings these shales into Beresford Dale to the north-west of Frank's Rock, and it can be seen that the Namurian beds rest unconformably upon the limestones, a state of affairs which we have previously noted along the western margin of the Peak District Namurian/Dinantian junction. The outcrop of shales in Beresford Dale extends just to the east of the river for a short distance, and on the right bank their impermeability accounts for the poor drainage of the land with swampy conditions close to the river.

Proceeding southwards along the flood-plain of the River Dove from Frank's Rock, well bedded purplish-grey and light-grey limestones are seen along the left bank. These beds belong to the Wolfscote Dale Limestone; they dip upstream at a low angle and disappear beneath the Alsop Moor Limestone. Fossils are very scarce in these beds some of which can be traced for considerable distances along the sides of the dale. No diagnostic fossils have been found in the Wolfscote Dale Limestone, but in view of their relationship to the Alsop Moor Limestone, the formation may be of lower D_1 age.

Southwards from Frank's Rock on the right bank of the Dove is Drabber Tor, a high bluff composed of fairly thickly bedded pale-grey limestones without chert, referred to as the Iron Tor Limestone, a formation at least 215m thick, on account of the good exposure at Iron Tors farther south on the left bank. For the most part these limestones are fine-grained and carry crinoid debris; some beds are porcellanous and could be called calcite mudstone or calcilutite. These beds appear to be of massif facies though there is a tendency to reef conditions locally; it is unfortunate that fossils are sparse and that diagnostic ones are absent. The Iron Tor Limestone must be older than the Wolfscote Dale Limestone, but beyond this the only possibility of dating them appears to be through the dating of the Dove Dale Limestone to the south, into which they appear to pass.

Just at a point where the River Dove curves sharply to the west and then back to the south-east there are some excellent exposures in the Iron Tors Limestone, and a little farther to the south these beds can be seen to pass insensibly into the massive reef limestones called the Dove Dale Limestone. From this point to Lode Mill on the Alsop-en-le-Dale to Alstonfield road, exposures are mainly in this reef limestone, and the latter in fact occupies most of the ground between Lode Mill and Thorpe Cloud near Ilam, five kilometres to the south.

It is advisable, unless time is no object, to walk up the path to the main road at Lode Mill and then to proceed south-westwards to Milldale. Along the roadside are exposures of well bedded light-grey to black limestones with bands and lenticles of chert. Some of the beds are dolomitised and there is a bed of true dolomite about one metre thick which can be followed for several hundred metres along the hillside south of Milldale. Fossils are infrequent here but a few fossils from the same beds near Nab's Spring farther south in Dove Dale, which include *Pustula nodosa* Thomas, suggests that the Milldale Limestone formation, to which these beds belong, is to be referred to the C zone. (Holkerian Stage)

That the Milldale Limestone beds are about the same age as the Dove Dale Limestone reefs can be seen at the high bluff known as

Fig 68   Dove Holes, Dovedale, Derbyshire

Raven's Tor on the right bank of the River Dove about a kilometre south of Milldale. Standing on the footpath on the left bank it can be observed that there is a gradual transition between the groups of limestones of the basin and reef facies.

Nab's Dale enters from the east a little farther south, and the exposure at Nab's Spring has already been referred to. Close by are the Dove Holes, two impressive caves in the reef limestone on the left bank of the river, formed at a time when the water-table was at a higher level than it is now (Figure 68).

South of Dove Holes, the rising ground on the right bank of the river appears to be mainly of basin-facies limestones, belonging to the Milldale Limestone, but on the left bank which carries the footpath somewhat higher reef limestones are splendidly exposed in the massive cliffs from Pickering Tor to Reynard's Cave and southwards to Tissington Spires. The lower reef limestones in this area yield *Levitusia humerosa* J. Sowerby which suggests a C_2 age for these beds in the Dove Dale Limestone. Between Tissington Spires and Lovers' Leap, farther downstream, dark-grey to black fine-grained limestones appear again; in the vicinity of Lovers' Leap these again appear to pass gradually into reef limestone.

That part of Dove Dale between Raven's Tor in the north and Lovers' Leap to the south is undoubtedly the most impressive from a scenic point of view. The reef limestones, owing to their massive and rather homogeneous character, have weathered to produce remarkable shapes, and at Reynard's Cave there is a fine natural arch ahead of the cave entrance. The view up the dale from the entrance to Reynard's Cave is one of the most superb in the whole of the Peak District.

REEF LIMESTONES OF THORPE CLOUD AND BUNSTER

To the south of Lovers' Leap the valley of the Dove is marked out by the conical hill of Thorpe Cloud on the east, and the almost equally impressive Bunster Hill on the west. Both are composed of the reef limestones of the Dove Dale Limestone which is at least 270m thick in exposed sections. These reef limestones are as usual light-grey in colour and fine-grained in texture, though there is much crinoidal debris at some horizons. Throughout the dale, the reef limestone has appeared as an immensely thick tabular mass with very occasional bedding planes, and with a fauna having a predominantly reef aspect. Nowhere within the Dove Dale Limestone is there the slightest suggestion of the development of reef knolls which are such a feature at this horizon in the Clitheroe district of Lancashire.

Bunster Hill and Thorpe Cloud appear to be reef knolls, that is immense piles of calcareous material which accumulated on the sea-floor in C zone times. Apart from the fossils which are locally very abundant the impalpable calcareous mud must have been trapped in a network of organisms, bryozoa, algae and sponges. Only in this way could the structure have continued to stand up under water with surface gradients far in excess of that which would be permitted with very fine loose material. Within the growing reef there were cavities which came to be occupied by communities of organisms, represented now (as far as those which secreted shells or tests are concerned) by the localised pockets of well preserved fossils.

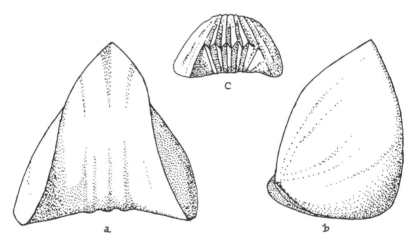

Fig 69 *Pugnax* spp. from the Dinantian reef limestones. a, *Pugnax acuminatus* (J. Sowerby), anterior view showing V-shaped commissure; b, lateral view of same specimen; c, *P. pugnus* (Martin), anterior view showed the serrated commissure. All natural size

On Thorpe Cloud a semblance of crude bedding can sometimes be seen, especially on the western slope, but none of these surfaces can be traced very far. Bands of reef-breccia appear to lie almost parallel to the present surface.

The top of Thorpe Cloud has been known as an excellent locality for fossils for more than a century. The limestone is very shelly and is of a type little known in reefs at this horizon of the Dinantian elsewhere in Britain. The fossils are well preserved, easily extracted, and can be collected in large numbers. The fauna is a large one mainly of brachiopods, the commonest brachiopods being *Spirifer bollandensis* Muir-Wood, *Reticularia lobata* Muir-Wood, and *Pugnax* spp. (Figure 69). The highest beds contain occasional specimens of the tabulate coral *Michelinia megastoma* (Phillips). The fauna confirms that these Dove Dale reef limestones are roughly the same age as those of Lancashire.

Thorpe Cloud and Bunster were formerly covered by the higher Dinantian limestones but a great deal of this was probably removed by pre-Namurian denudation. The subsequent Upper Carboniferous cover was probably removed by Middle Triassic times since when there have been slight modifications of the topography.

CHAPTER 13

Chrome Hill and Parkhouse Hill

About ten kilometres south-east of Buxton and flanking the River Dove on its north side is a line of impressive hills, High Wheeldon near Crowdecote, Aldery Cliff, Hitter Hill, Parkhouse Hill, Chrome Hill and Tor Rock. They are all composed of reef limestones, Parkhouse Hill and Chrome Hill having most fantastic shapes from whichever direction they are viewed (Figure 70).

To the east of these hills are the largely quarried areas of Hillhead, Hindlow and Earlsterndale, all in thickly but well bedded limestone carrying fossils indicative of the D_1 zone.

To the west of the hills of reef limestone is the eastern edge of an extensive outcrop of Namurian rocks, many of them shales but some including sandstones such as the thick Longnor Sandstone or Grit which caps Hollins Hill, and which can be traced northwestwards to Landmanlow where its thin representative is seen to be overlain by a

Fig 70   View looking south-west from Jericho Quarry, Earlsterndale. In the foreground are bedded limestones, exposed in Glutton Dale below the crossroads. Beyond are two spectacular hills in reef limestones, Parkhouse Hill in the centre just breaking the skyline and Chrome Hill up on the right. The country beyond is in Namurian rocks including the wave-like Longnor Edge on the left which is capped by sandstone

142

marine band with *Reticuloceras bilingue*. The relationships of the massif limestones to the reefs, and of the Namurian strata to the reefs, can be observed in the field.

In approaching this area from Buxton, by the road to Ashbourne, detached outcrops of lava are seen at Staden Low to the north and at Fox Low to the south of the road, two kilometres south-east of Buxton. These outliers of lava have been shown to belong to the Lower Lava of the Wye Valley by the finding, some ten metres below the base of the flow, of the *Davidsonina septosa* band. The underlying limestones farther to the south-east are therefore the Chee Tor Limestones of D_1 age; they can be seen at Hillhead and near Brierlow Bar. Turning right at the Bar, along the road towards the village of Earlsterndale, poorly fossiliferous well bedded light-grey limestones can be seen as gently dipping scars on the hillsides. The dip is westerly towards the Namurian ground which can be seen in that direction. Large amounts of these limestones have been quarried in this district mainly for the production of lime, and limekilns are a feature of the landscape.

In the direction of Earlsterndale the road forks at Jericho, and the small disused Jericho Quarry is seen immediately on the left. It shows a good exposure of the *D. septosa* band. Evidence of turbulent

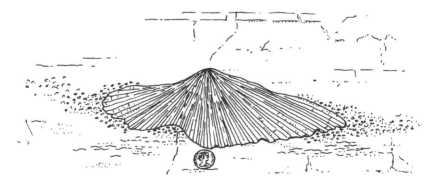

Fig 71 Existence of turbulent conditions during deposition of Chee Tor limestones about the horizon of the *Davidsonina septosa* band, indicated by overturned corallum of *Lithostrotion* sp., Jericho Quarry, Earlsterndale, Derbyshire. Notice comminuted crinoid material around corallum

conditions during the deposition of these limestones is seen in a few large coralla of colonial corals which are inverted (Figure 71). The beds dip towards Glutton Dale which is traversed by the road to Longnor.

At the head of Glutton Dale, close to the cross-roads and on the north-west flank of Hitter Hill, well bedded light-grey limestones with a D_1 fauna are exposed, and it seems likely that they are not far above the *D. septosa* band. Down the flanks of the gently winding Glutton Dale the D_1 limestones are seen to persist in their bedded nature as far as the point where the road suddenly assumes a higher gradient. High up in the cliffs on the right bank of the dale the limestones yield a fauna of productid and spiriferid brachiopods quite unusual in the massif facies at this horizon. A little farther down the dale the limestones quickly lose their bedding, and they pass into unbedded

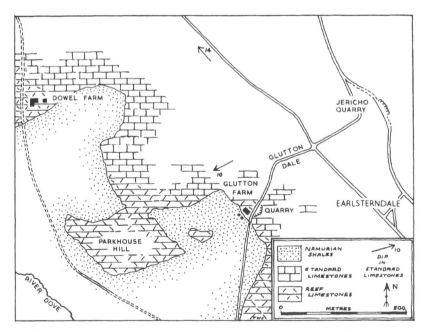

Fig 72   Geological sketch-map of the area around Parkhouse Hill and Glutton Dale near Earlsterndale. *Crown Copyright reserved*

reef-like limestone which is clearly seen in the abandoned quarry on the left-hand side of the road near the bottom of the dale, close to Glutton Farm. The fauna is a mixed one; it includes the typical D_1 fossil *Palaeosmilia murchisoni*, present in the massif limestones to the east, and occasional goniatites indicating the B_2 zone in the basin facies. This Glutton Dale section provides one of the clearest examples of the rapid passage of normal bedded limestones into reef limestones. Other outstanding sections in the Peak District in this connexion are in the Winnats Pass in the Castleton area (p 92) and near Iron Tors in Dove Dale (p 135).

Close behind Glutton Farm to the north-west is the striking Parkhouse Hill. It is a mass of reef limestone, steep on all sides, but particularly on its eastern side; there the steep limestone slope descends to a broad low col bounded by bedded limestones on its eastern side. The transition from bedded to reef limestones might be expected in this depression, but examination quickly shows that the col is floored with blue and grey shales of Namurian age (Figure 72). This is an intra-Carboniferous unconformity of considerable dimensions; possibly a thickness of at least 300m of limestone was denuded from this area before the Namurian shales were laid down.

The feather-edge of Namurian shales can be traced round the southern and on to the western slopes of Parkhouse Hill. That these shales extend uphill very much farther than the main change of slope has been proved by observing the material thrown out of rabbit burrows prior to the advent of myxomatosis. To the west of the hill the Namurian shales thicken and are exposed in places along the banks of the River Dove. They are well exposed by the river opposite the northern end of Parkhouse Hill, and their outcrop expands to fill a miniature intermontane basin to the south of Dowel Farm.

Parkhouse Hill consists of fine-grained reef limestones containing nests of well preserved fossils in places. Many of the most beautiful Lower Carboniferous brachiopods preserved in Great Britain were found here and neighbouring Chrome Hill, such as specimens of *Dielasma saccula* showing original colour-banding.

From the top of Parkhouse Hill, it is convincingly seen that the limestone is surrounded through at least three-quarters of its circumference by Namurian shales. In other words the hill is almost an island of limestone in a sea of shale.

Dowel Dale to the north-east of Dowel Farm, like Glutton Dale, shows fossiliferous reef limestones passing eastwards into well bedded light grey limestones including the *D. septosa* band.

Chrome Hill, also famed for its reef limestone fossils of B_2 age, may be ascended from the north-east, in which direction the Namurian shales pass well up its flanks. The reef limestones are similar to those of Parkhouse Hill, and there are some well developed reef breccias exposed on the west side of Chrome Hill just below the summit. The sandstone capping Hollins Hill to the west must have been deposited against the western flanks of Chrome Hill.

In this area there is startling evidence of pre-Namurian denudation of the Viséan limestones. The country we now see is a pre-Namurian landscape which has been buried and now largely re-excavated.

CHAPTER 14

The Valley of the River Manifold

Unlike the River Dove which marks the boundary between the counties of Derbyshire and Staffordshire, the valley of the River Manifold lies wholly within the latter county.

The River Manifold rises within a kilometre of the Dove, in a field behind the Travellers' Rest Inn on the east side of the Buxton–Leek road near the village of Flash on the eastern slopes of Axe Edge. From its source to Hulme End about three kilometres west-south-west of Hartington the River Manifold has cut a valley in Lower Namurian rocks and this is roughly parallel to the valley of the River Dove. At Hulme End, the River Manifold enters the Dinantian limestone terrain and pursues a deeply entrenched meandering valley lying roughly five kilometres west of the River Dove near Wetton. At Beeston Tor to the south of Wetton the Manifold receives its main tributary, the River Hamps, on its right bank. The River Hamps rises to the north of Mixon, seven kilometres west-north-west of Wetton, and flowing southwards has excavated a valley in the N–S Mixon Anticline, a structure lying east of and *en échelon* with the Goyt Syncline. The Hamps Valley is responsible for an inlier of Carboniferous Limestone at Mixon consisting of thin limestones and shales of basin facies in the P_2 zone. At Onecote the Hamps veers to a south-easterly direction and, cutting through Lower Namurian sediments, goes on to Waterhouses on the Leek–Ashbourne road where it quickly changes its course first in an easterly direction and after a kilometre to a northerly direction until it joins the River Manifold. From Waterhouses the River Hamps runs through the Carboniferous Limestone. There has been a considerable amount of river capture in the whole of the Manifold–Dove region. The whole region is essentially a deeply incised plateau whose summit plain lies about 350m above sea-level. In the Hamps and Manifold valleys the depth of the valley often exceeds 150m.

The River Manifold has excavated a valley of great beauty between Hulme End and Ilam where it joins the River Dove. The rocks are all limestones and subsidary shales representing the basin facies, and masses of reef limestone attributed to the marginal or reef facies of the Dinantian. Very broadly this section of the valley is cut through a large anticline, but the detailed structure as well as the lithology is complex. In particular the immense masses of reef limestone, which give rise to some of the more spectacular cliffs and bluffs, have suffered little during folding; they have acted as immense bastions in the succession with the result that the less-competent thinly bedded limestones and shales have yielded to produce complicated folded and faulted structures.

A splendid section of limestones with shaly partings, of basin facies and probably D_1 in age, is to be seen in a chain of old quarries along the roadside on the left bank of the River Manifold at Apes Tor (Figure 73). This may be reached by taking the Alstonfield road from Hulme End and turning to the right after about 400m; the road turns

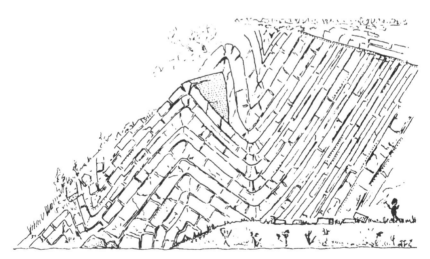

Fig 73 Sharply folded limestones with shaly partings at Apes Tor, Manifold Valley near Warslow, Staffordshire. A thrust is visible at the top of the quarry on the right

to the left through a farmyard, and beyond the next right-hand bend the section begins on the left.

The well bedded dark-grey limestones with chert and with carbonaceous shale partings are folded into a series of slightly asymmetrical anticlines and synclines. The crests and troughs are acute and the plunges of the folds can be measured. The fold axes trend north-north-west. At the west end of the section, at the top of the cliff, a low-angle thrust is visible.

Farther down the valley, a narrow road negotiable by vehicles enters from Warslow on the right, and looking southwards on the left is Ecton Hill, the site of the famous but long-disused Ecton Copper Mine. The workings are very extensive and were entered by adits as well as deep shafts, some of which are now flooded. The ore bodies in the form of veins and pipes carried large quantities of chalcopyrite with subsidiary galena. Immense tonnages of copper ore were removed, a great deal of the metal produced being used in the hulls of ships. It is said that the Crescent in Buxton was built out of a single year's profits from the Ecton mines.

Some spoil heaps, such as the one encircled by a fence on the hillside above the road, yield occasional specimens of chalcopyrite, azurite, and malachite. On the roadside below are modern workings in calcrete, a limestone scree in which the angular pieces of limestone have been cemented together by calcium carbonate deposited from ground water. This is a Recent deposit.

Continuing along the road towards Butterton, about a kilometre south of the calcrete workings, a gate on the left gives vehicle-access to the remainder of the valley of the Manifold. The road with two further gates leads along the western flank of Ecton Hill and the Sugar Loaf to Wettonmill. The limestones and mudstones exposed sporadically along this road are of Upper Viséan age.

At Wettonmill reef limestones are entered and from here to Ilam the personality of the valley varies with the seasons and with the weather. Prior to 1933 there was a light railway through the valley from Hulme End to Waterhouses where there was a connection for Leek. This railway was used not only by tourists, but by the local farmers for taking their produce to market and for bringing in their equipment and foodstuffs. There was a regular service each day, but the line was closed when increasing competition from road transport rendered the line uneconomic. Before the rails and sleepers were removed in 1933, the track was used for the trials of some diesel locomotives being built for export. The old track was presented by the railway company to the county and the present footpath was built along it. This footpath goes southwards as far as Beeston Tor. Cars are not allowed on the metalled footpath, but there are convenient car-parks at Wettonmill near the ford, and at Redhurst Crossing where the road from Wetton reaches the river.

The village of Wetton forms a good alternative route into the valley. The church is worthy of a visit; geologists might be interested to see the grave, near the east window, of Samuel Carrington, for many years the village schoolmaster, famous for his collections of local Carboniferous Limestone fossils, many of them now in museums. The tombstone is decorated with carvings of fossils such as *Productus* and *Nautilus*, somewhat stylised (Figure 74).

The road from Wetton to Redhurst Crossing is narrow and steep but full of interest. Having negotiated a left- and a right-hand bend there is a panoramic view of the valley with the church spires in the villages of Grindon and Butterton standing out beyond Ossom's Hill and Thor's Cave. A couple of dewponds are passed. Dew-ponds, formerly of frequent occurrence in the limestone country of the Peak District, were artificial shallow basins lined with straw and mud. The dew was supposed to condense in them and to maintain the level of

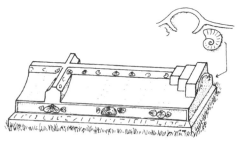

Fig 74   Tombstone on the grave of Samuel Carrington in the churchyard at Wetton, Staffordshire

the pond. Certainly it is extraordinary how some dew-ponds still contain some water even after a period of drought. Modern dew-ponds are lined with concrete, but they still appear to function.

Upon reaching Redhurst Crossing the air may be pervaded with the sound of running water as the river rushes in spate over its rocky bed, or there may be a strange silence if the bed of the river is dry. The River Manifold has an underground course through a connected system of caverns. The water can be observed to plunge underground from its bed at a point where a leftward swing of the river brings it against a limestone bluff a short distance below Wettonmill. There is also a large intake from the bed of the river a little farther south, where the Manifold is cutting into the base of Ossom's Hill just south of the humped road-bridge between Wetton Mill and Redhurst Crossing.

In the dry season the Wettonmill sinks may take the whole of the water. In the wet season it is clear that although both set of sinks may be operating to the full, the underground system can not cope with all the water in the river. When the river bed is dry at Redhurst Crossing the water is not seen again until it comes bubbling up into the river bed in the grounds of Ilam Hall. The water has travelled underground for about five kilometres.

The River Hamps also is carried entirely underground for part of its length above Beeston Tor during dry weather. Many years ago, the author was camping at the confluence of the Hamps and the Manifold near Beeston Tor. It was high summer, the river beds were dry, and except for the light railway there was barely a sound in the valley. There was a day of heavy thunderstorms but these had ceased just about sunset. At about 3am the author was wakened by a sudden gale and a long-continued noise like an express steam-train. Immense walls of water were coming down the valleys of the Manifold and the Hamps. These walls met near the confluence and it was seen that they were carrying uprooted trees and several sheep. The noise of running water reigned for little more than two days and then silence returned to the valley.

As in Dove Dale, so in the Manifold Valley the most impressive elements of the landscape are due to reef limestones. The upstanding masses of reef limestone at Thor's Cave, Beeston Tor, and Nanny Tor contrast markedly with the limestones and mudstones out of which they seem to rise. Each mass of reef limestone appears to be dome-shaped with a gently curved top and very steep if not verical flanks. Each may reach a height of 100m or more. The bedded limestones around each mass of reef dip away in peripheral fashion, and owing to shearing along the junction brought about during folding it is difficult to find one where the relationship between reef and bedded limestone can be studied in detail and decisively. However, the mass of reef forming Beeston Tor just below the River Hamps confluence can be examined in the river bed about thirty metres east of Beeston Tor Cottage. Calcareous mudstones without any perceptible dip can be traced to within a few metres of undoubted reef limestone. Between the two is a remarkable breccia consisting of angular fragments of limestone in a dark-grey siliceous matrix; close to the reef the included angular blocks or clasts are large, some over a metre in diameter, but farther away the fragments are smaller. Evidently, the reef stood high above the level of the sea floor and blocks broken off fell into the calcareous and siliceous mud which was being deposited around the reef. The Beeston Tor reef yields an extensive fauna mainly of brachiopods and a specimen of the

Fig 75   Thor's Cave, Manifold Valley, viewed from the north on the road from Wetton to Redhurst Crossing

goniatite *Pericyclus fasciculatus* (McCoy) has been found. This may indicate a C_1 age for the lowest reef and associated calcareous mudstones.

Beeston Tor contains several caves including St Bertram's Cave, Hayhole and Jackadaw's Cave.

The most famous cave in the Manifold Valley is Thor's Cave. Situated high above the river on the left bank, about 800m south of Redhurst Crossing, it has an impressive entrance facing north (Figure 75) which can be reached either from the road to Wetton or by crossing the footbridge over the river below it and climbing the hill. The interior of the cave receives light from another entrance called the West Window. The deposits in the cave floor were excavated many years ago; they were not removed systematically, and consequently the fauna recorded is a composite one covering many thousands of years. It includes bear, hyena, and sabre-toothed tiger plus more recent inhabitants including man.

A short distance to the south and below the West Window of Thor's Cave is the Fissure Cave which was excavated half a century ago; the deposits yielded human jaws, worked flints and bone implements, and the remains of bear, giant deer, wolf, ox, and polecat, followed by pieces of pottery and jewellery indicating occupation during the Bronze Age, the Iron Age, and in Roman times.

There is no evidence in the Manifold Valley area of standard limestones of massif type such as are found to the east of Dove Dale. It was in that direction that the edge of the rigid block lay. The base of the Lower Carboniferous is not seen, and its position is quite unknown in the Manifold–Dove country. The succession is a thick one beginning in the Manifold Valley with beds of C zone age. There is no specific evidence of representatives of the S zone and it has been suggested both in the Manifold and in the Dove valleys that thick D_1 beds rest unconformably upon the beds below. In other words, the late Tournaisian and early Viséan limestones were folded and partly denuded before beds of D_1 age were laid down.

There is evidence too that the whole of the Dinantian succession was uplifted and denuded in pre-Namurian times, and it seems very likely that the landscape close to the Namurian outcrops in the Manifold Valley region, particularly around Butterton, Ford, Waterfall, Gateham and Hopedale, is a pre-Namurian one which has been uncovered.

CHAPTER 15

The Roaches and Goldsitch Moss

The Goyt Syncline, the first major structure to the west of the Dinantian-Namurian unconformable boundary, to the north and south of Buxton, can be traced from north of Ludworth southwards almost to Leek with possibly an extension into the Cheadle coalfield, a distance of at least forty kilometres. Throughout most of its course this pronounced fold affects Upper Namurian rocks at the surface; as these consist of an alternation of thick sandstones or grits and shales the structure is easily picked out in the landscape. On the western limb of the syncline the sandstone escarpments or edges face to the west, while the opposite is true on the eastern limb. The opposing dip-slopes, frequently mantled by deposits of peat, serve to accentuate the close relationship between surface and structure (Figure 76).

Fig 76   The Goyt Syncline at Goldsitch Moss viewed from the north at Cutthorn Hill near Three Shires Head. The highest point is the Roaches with the dip slope of the Roaches Grit to the left of the summit

Nowhere is the structure more readily discernible than in the high moorland country of Goldsitch Moss and its southern limit marked by the striking sandstone escarpment of the Roaches about eight kilometres to the north of Leek. The synclinal structure is easily appreciated in approaching the area from the south along the main road from Leek. After crossing the River Churnet the road climbs steeply up Cat Tor, the new road by-passing the hamlet of Upper Hulme. When the gradient decreases the eastward-facing bastion of massive and cross-bedded sandstones known as Ramshaw Rocks comes into view. These sandstones, known as the Roaches Sandstone or Grit, are the equivalent of the Ashover Sandstone or Grit. Both are succeeded by a marine band carrying the goniatite *Reticuloceras superbilingue*. The sandstones are pale buff to purplish-brown in colour, with coarse sharp grains of quartz, a considerable amount of feldspar, and scattered sub-angular to rounded quartz pebbles. The sandstone has pene-contemporaneous channels in places and a study of the cross-bedding shows that the material had a general northerly source. That much of it was deposited quickly is evident from the occasional fossil plant such as a large tree-branch which may be found lying almost perpendicularly to the normal bedding. The detritus making up the sandstone must obviously have been derived from a granitic terrain lying far to the north, and it was brought

Fig 77 Weird erosional features in the Roaches Sandstone at Ramshaw Rocks on the Buxton–Leek road, viewed from below

southwards by powerful rivers which becoming anastomose or braided, deposited it in shifting sand-banks at a small altitude above sea-level.

The Roaches Sandstone can be examined at Ramshaw Rocks where it has been denuded into fantastic shapes which must have been produced during a weathering regime different from that prevailing today (Figure 77).

If one drives northwards up the road alongside Ramshaw Rocks the Old Lady of Ramshaw Rocks may be seen. 'She' is a relatively thin joint-slab of sandstone eroded into the profile of a human head. There is a hole in the slab roughly where the eye should be in side view. As one passes a hawthorn tree on the left-hand side of the road, the Old Lady is seen to wink. This is due to the traveller viewing rock-sky-rock through the hole in quick succession.

Traced southwards, the outcrop of the Roaches Sandstone largely represented in an impressive escarpment bends round to the west through the separate fault-bounded hill of Hen Cloud, then north-westwards so that the immense scarps of Five Clouds and the Roaches face in a southwesterly direction. This marked V-shaped outcrop readily visible on the one-inch Ordnance Survey map, or on aerial photographs, shows that in this particular area the Goyt Syncline has an appreciable plunge to the north. Good views of the outcrop of the Roaches Sandstone and the beds which immediately overlie it are obtainable from points on the road leading from the top of Ramshaw to Warslow, or by taking the narrow lane leading westwards from the cottage where the road from Leek first begins to run parallel to Ramshaw Rocks. Upon turning right after a short climb one can look westwards down the dip-slope of the Roaches Sandstone, see the same dipslope rising to the skyline on the opposite limb of the syncline, and observe the southerly pointing V-shaped outcrop of the next higher sandstone (the Chatsworth Sandstone or Grit) lying below the *Gastrioceras cancellatum* band (Figure 78).

These, and higher beds, are best examined in the small ancient coalfield area of Goldsitch Moss to the north. This is best approached from the Leek–Buxton road turning left about 400m south of the Royal Cottage Inn along the road signposted 'Quarnford'. Immedi-

Fig 78   View across the northerly-plunging Goyt Syncline, looking westwards from Ramshaw Rocks on the Buxton–Leek road. In the foreground is part of the dip-slope of the Roaches sandstone; the opposing dip-slope of this sandstone on the other limb of the syncline is seen against the skyline. In the middle distance is the V-shaped outcrop of the sandstone (Chatsworth Grit or Sandstone) below the *Gastrioceras cancellatum* marine band

ately, beyond boggy ground, a low eastward-facing scarp of sandstone is seen. This is the Roaches Sandstone, which can be traced continuously northwards from Ramshaw Rocks, and which has diminished in thickness considerably. Continuing along the road and bearing right at the next junction one descends to a bridge over a stream. This tributary of the westerly-flowing River Dane is called the Black Brook. Rising near Gib Tor to the north-east of the bridge it provides a useful section from the Roaches Sandstone, upwards through the equivalent of the Chatsworth Sandstone to the *Gastrioceras cancellatum* marine band which is exposed about 250m above the bridge. Both sandstones form rugged features along the adjacent hillsides on this eastern limb of the Goyt Syncline and by looking in a south-westerly direction these same sandstones can be seen on the western limb. The Roaches Sandstone forms the high skyline and this is the dip-slope of the Roaches. Part way down this slope a secondary linear feature, partly masked by peat and a growth of heather and bilberry, marks the outcrop of the Chatsworth Sandstone.

Just above the bridge, flaggy pale-grey and cream sandstones are seen in the bed of the stream. That these are part of the uppermost Namurian sandstone, the Rough Rock, can be proved by the outcrop

100m or so south of the bridge of the *Gastrioceras subcrenatum* marine band. This is the internationally agreed upper limit of the Namurian. The marine band is usually poorly exposed here but the contorted bed which occurs above it (p 84) crops out on both banks of the stream.

It will be noticed that the Rough Rock, another product of a fluvial environment, gives rise to a very weak feature. The Rough Rock is extremely variable in its resistance to denudation, partly owing to the variability in the degree of cementation of the sand grains. In spite of this, the outcrop of the Rough Rock can be traced with ease on both limbs of the syncline. On the west limb, the Rough Rock and the marine band above it is well exposed in the bed of and right bank of the Black Brook 400m west-north-west of Goldsitch Houses.

THE ROUGH ROCK OF QUARNFORD AND GOLDSITCH

Undoubtedly the best exposure of the top of the Rough rock and the beds immediately above it is situated in the right bank of a stream cutting through the eastern limb of the syncline, just north of the Wash at Quarnford, two kilometres north-north-west of the bridge on Golsitch Moss. The following section is seen:

	metres
Blue and grey shale	1.00
Contorted bed	0.35
Marine band	0.32
Shale	0.75
Coal	0.07
Fireclay	2.00
Cross-bedded sandstone	6.00+

The strata above the *Gastrioceras subcrenatum* marine band are referred to the Coal Measure or Westphalian. In the coalfields to the west and east of the Peak District these coal-bearing beds reach thickness in excess of 2,000m. Of this considerable thickness, all that remains in the Peak District are small outliers of the lowest Coal Measures preserved in subsidiary synclines. The Goyt Syncline includes such outliers along its whole length. Attention has already been drawn to the small long-abandoned coalfield of Goyt's Moss (p 82). A similar outlier is present on Goldsitch Moss and some of the strata can be seen in the stream section near Goldsitch Houses. Goldsitch Moss abounds in small spoil heaps of shale with fragments of coal and deep depressions marking the sites of shafts. In the Geological Survey memoir entitled *The Geology of the Country around Stockport, Macclesfield, Congleton and Leek* (1866) the coal workings on Goldsitch Moss are described as 'ancient'. No doubt the coal was used mainly for the burning of limestone in the Buxton area.

To-day, Goldsitch Moss is quiet and peaceful. Away from a main road its better-drained parts are used as meadows by the few small scattered farms, each of which keeps a few head of cattle and some sheep. The wild hillsides give shelter to a few grouse, and buzzards, kestrels, curlew, snipe, and lapwing are common. No spring passes without the cuckoo paying a visit.

Undoubtedly it is one of the most instructive areas not only in the Peak District, but in Great Britain, for beginners in geology.

NAMURIAN SUCCESSIONS IN THE PEAK DISTRICT

Although there is a marked similarity in the Upper Namurian successions all around the Peak District, correlation on the basis of the widespread marine bands shows that not only may there be rapid lateral changes, such as the attenuation or thickening of sandstones, but there are also considerable changes in general thicknesses. The Upper Namurian sandstones are all deposits of a terrestrial, alluvial and, at times, deltaic environment and there is little to suggest that the geotropically negative basin and positive massif areas which were reflected through much of Dinantian time, operated during late Namurian time. Such is not, however, the case in earlier Namurian time.

It is not, of course, possible to examine Lower Namurian strata all around the Peak District. It has already been seen that north and south of Buxton there is a marked unconformity between the Namurian and the Dinantian and that a great deal of the Namurian sequence may be cut out by overlap. For example, at Ladmanlow south of Buxton an attenuated representative of the Longnor Sandstone with *Reticuloceras bilingue* in the marine band above it rests directly upon eroded Dinantian limestones (p 76).

North of Castleton, at Alport and Edale, boreholes have proved thick marine Namurian sequences apparently conformably succeeding basin facies sediments of Dinantian age. The great distinguishing features between the sedimentation on the massif and in the basin had broken down long before the end of Dinantian time. In the Wye Valley section, for example, we find that massif-facies limestones of D_2 age (based upon corals and brachiopods) are succeeded by basin-type sediments in which the goniatites and bivalves denote a P_2 age (p 71).

The Namurian-Dinantian unconformity seems to denote not so much a matter of pre-Namurian folding of the limestone sequence, as an uplift of the massif or part of it followed by pre-Namurian denudation. This we have seen is well authenticated all down the western side of the Dinantian massif, from Sparrowpit southwards to Buxton, Parkhouse Hill, Crowdecote and the Manifold Valley.

It has been noticed that on the eastern margins of the Peak District a Namurian-Dinantian unconformity probably does not exist, and that there was continuous sedimentation from P_2 to E_1 times (p 132).

At the end of P_2 times differential movement of the massif, which had been in abeyance for some time, was resuscitated. It is possible that only the western edge of the massif, marked by a line of Dinantian reefs, rose to be denuded subsequently. It seems much more likely, however, that the massif underwent a progressive tilt, rising in the west and subsiding in the east. Indeed, as stated above, an easterly subsidence had operated in P_2 times allowing basin-type sedimentation along the eastern side of the massif. This appears to have continued into earliest Namurian times in that area for in a small outlier of Namurian shales at Wardlow Mires about three kilometres east of Tideswell, basal Namurian sediments with the E_1 goniatite *Cravenoceras leion* were proved in a borehole put down by the British Geological Survey, though it is significant that the sequence is a condensed one. Some part of the P_2 limestone succession is missing there, and if the present topography around Wardlow Mires is regarded as an exhumed pre-Namurian topography then some pre-Namurian denudation had occurred, though not as severe as along the western edge of the massif.

Lower Namurian sediments are exposed in the country to the east and south-east of the Roaches particularly in the valleys of the Rivers Churnet, Dove, Hamps, and Manifold. This is a country of deep valleys cutting broad areas of rather featureless heather-clad moorlands. The structures are complex, but the main folds are on N–S axes. Recent work has shown that after the post-Dinantian uplift and denudation in the west, the roles of basin and massif were re-established. The early Namurian successions in the basin areas are very much thicker than on the massif. The differential subsidence between the two areas was marked. In the basin areas the early Namurian sediments are fine calcareous sandstones and siltstones, mudstones and shales with goniatite-lamellibranch faunas representing the zones E_1, E_2, H, and R_1. There are also fine and medium-grained orthoquartzitic and protoquartzitic sandstones. Some of the beds appear to be turbidites, and bear sole-structures which leave no doubt that the material originated in the south, probably from the rivers draining the northern slopes of St George's Land. The sediments lack the potassium feldspars and garnets which are so characteristic of the northerly-derived upper Namurian fluvial sandstones.

To the north of Castleton some turbidite sediments were also deposited during part of lower Namurian time, but there the sediments provide incontrovertible evidence that they were derived from the north.

The latitude of Buxton appears to be a very approximate line along which very attenuated representatives of northerly- and southerly-derived sand-bodies interdigitated in the lower Namurian sequence of generally marine sediments.

About six kilometres west-north-west of Upper Hulme on the Leek–Buxton road is Gun Hill, a sweeping hill rising to an altitude of 400m above sea-level. The upper parts of the hill are formed of well bedded light-grey or white orthoquartzites of Lower Namurian, E_2 age, and the structure is that of an anticline with a N–S axis and plunging at each end. The Gun Hill Anticline is parallel to and lies *en échelon* with the Goyt Syncline. Gun Hill is an unusual case in that a hill coincides with an anticline.

In 1938 a deep borehole was put down near the top of Gun Hill in a search for petroleum. It passed through the E zone of the Namurian to a depth of about 300m which latter approximates to the *Cravenoceras leion* horizon; below this, the borehole entered basin facies sediments of highest Dinantian P_2 age. As the beds assumed an increasingly high dip with continuing depth, boring ceased at a depth of 1300m.

Like the Alport and Edale borings, this one at Gun Hill was important in the development of the block-basin hypothesis. It also provides valuable evidence regarding the rate of subsidence and sedimentation in an early Namurian basin area. For example, at Gun Hill sediments representing the E_1 zone are roughly 270m thick. At Ashover on the eastern edge of the massif only just over ten metres of sediments were deposited during the same time. This is a measure of the differential subsidence as between basin and massif.

This extensive subsidence and sedimentation in the basin area persisted until R_1 times when fluvial deposition spread from the north accompanied possibly by subsidiary contributions from the southern land-mass.

Whether this was the end of depositional control by the relative tectonic behaviour of massif and basin is difficult to say. Certainly the basin-massif orientation seemed to exercise little control during the deposition of the higher beds of the Namurian.

It so happens that the earliest sediments which accumulated on the massif form the essential core of the Peak District. To east and to west the basin facies has been proved. Were the existence of this facies to be proved far below the Derbyshire and Cheshire-North Staffordshire coalfields on the two sides of the Peak District, then it might be surmised that these areas were geotropically negative in Coal Measures times, and that massif and basin were still effective to some extent. Any such suggestion would upset computations as to the thickness of the Upper Carboniferous cover which has been removed from the central part of the Peak District.

CHAPTER 16

Kinder Scout

Situated to the north of a line through Whaley Bridge and Chapel-en-le-Frith is a very extensive area of the Pennines a great deal of which lies at an altitude of more than 500m above sea-level. It is composed entirely of rocks of Namurian age having a broad anticlinal structure about a general N–S axis. It is largely high desolate moorland country with extensive sphagnum mosses and cotton-grass hollows and lines of sandstone scarps or edges, deeply dissected by the numerous head streams of the Rivers Noe, Goyt, and Etherow which drain eventually to the Irish Sea, and the Derwent and Little Don which are bound for the North Sea.

The southern part of this immense upland area lying in the triangle formed by the Glossop–Bamford, Glossop to Chapel-on-le-Frith and Chapel-en-le-Frith to Castleton roads, is known as the High Peak. It includes the highest summits which are almost 700m above sea-level, such as Kinder Scout, Kinder Low, and Crowden Head.

This high moorland country is a plateau of gently dipping beds, all belonging to the R_1 zone of the Namurian. These are

Kinder Scout Grit or Sandstone
Shale Grit
Mam Tor Beds

In a previous chapter it has been seen that the Mam Tor Beds succeed the Edale Shales (p 97), and that in the valley of the River Noe exposures of the Edale Shales range from E_2 to basal R_1 in age, whilst the Edale borehole showed that these shales actually extend to the base of the E_1 zone. The junction between the Edale Shales and the Mam Tor Beds can be seen at Mam Tor and can be traced all round the Vale of Edale. There is good reason to believe that the junction between predominantly arenaceous rocks above and argillaceous ones below is not everywhere at the same horizon. The ratio of sandstone to shale varies considerably from place to place, and in several localities beds of sandstone can be seen to pass laterally into shale. In other words, the junction between the Edale Shales and the Mam Tor Beds cuts across the time-planes. A formation or a boundary which behaves in this way is said to be diachronous (Figure 79). In much of the area around Kinder Scout where the Mam Tor Beds are exposed the sandstones are seen to bulk much less than at the type-locality of Mam Tor. The top of the beds is also diachronous so that the thickness of the formation as a whole is variable. For example it amounts to about seventy metres on the north side of the Vale of Edale and in the Alport and Ashop valleys, while the thickness is nearer to 150m at Mam Tor.

THE MAM TOR BEDS

In the type section of the Mam Tor Beds a repetition of a succession of lithologies has been observed. Each cyclic unit or

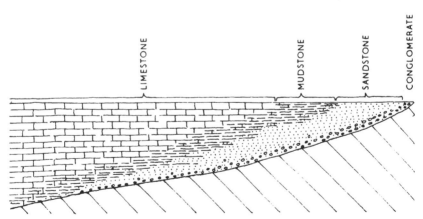

Fig 79 Simple diagrammatic representation of diachronism arising during a marine transgression. The vertical scale is greatly exaggerated relative to the horizontal. Time planes are horizontal. Formational boundaries cut across these time planes so that any one formation may vary considerably in age across the area of development

cyclothem consists of massive sandstone at the base, followed first by laminated sandstone, then by shale and mudstone. The thickness of a cyclothem varies from one to three metres. The base of each sandstone unit is very sharp and exhibits sole-markings the orientation of which indicates currents flowing from the north. The laminated sandstones frequently exhibit low-angle cross-bedding and ripple-drift, and graded bedding is also seen. It is believed that this kind of evidence indicates rapid deposition of the sandstones by intermittent turbidity currents carrying sediment to the distal end of the slopes of a delta which was being built out into a deep marine environment. In many localities the shale and mudstone unit in a cyclothem yields poor goniatite-bivalve faunas which inhabited this area. At some horizons submarine sliding or slumping is evidenced by corrugated bedding and slump-balls.

THE SHALE GRIT

The succeeding formation, the Shale Grit, was so-named many years ago on account of the fragments or pellets of shale which are often found in the sandstones. Sandstones predominate over shales and are often thick enough to produce lines of crags or even impressive escarpments. In fact, the shale partings seem to die out to the south so that where the Shale Grit was deposited in the area of the massif, sandstone alone is present; a good example is the sandstone forming Eyam Edge which exhibits a thickness of over sixty metres, contains no shale, and represents the Shale Grit.

The Shale Grit crops out extensively all around the Kinder Scout plateau. Except on steep slopes and in the beds of streams the outcrop is often covered with thick peat; where the sandstone units become thick the landscape becomes craggy.

The upper and lower boundaries of the Shale Grit are diachronous and the thickness of the formations shows marked variation. In the west of the Vale of Edale it is about 200m, but it thins considerably towards Hathersage. Good sections can be seen in the northern tributaries of the River Noe, and the valley from Upper Booth to Edale Head and Jacob's Ladder affords a useful traverse through typical Shale Grit country.

THE KINDER SCOUT GRIT

The Kinder Scout Grit or Sandstone forms the broad summit of the Kinder Scout plateau. It is an extraordinary arenaceous formation attaining a thickness of about 200m. It is, over much of the area, developed as two so-called 'leaves'; a lower one which is about 100m thick on the western side of Kinder Scout, consisting of coarse, feldspathic and often pebbly sandstones, massive or very thickly bedded; an upper leaf, from thirty to fifty metres thick on the west of Kinder Scout, consisting of thickly bedded or massive medium-grained sandstones, with bands containing shale pellets in places. Between the upper and lower Kinder Scout Grit there is usually a band of shales of variable thickness which may carry a marine band, the Butterly Marine Band, which contains molluscs and brachiopods.

The lower leaf of the Kinder Scout Grit is sometimes ganisteroid at the top with roots of *Stigmaria*, and a thin layer of coal appears here and there. There are several prominent but small outliers of this lower leaf, the most obvious in the landscape being Crook Hill and Win Hill.

The upper Kinder Scout Grit has its main outcrop immediately around Kinder Scout; if forms some very impressive north-facing edges such as The Edge and Blackden Edge. The base is very irregular in places and seems to fill channels scoured in the underlying shale, and this probably accounts for some of the variations in thickness of the shale between the upper and lower leaves. The upper surface is followed usually by a small thickness of shales and in places by a thin seat-earth and coal. Immediately above these beds is a marine band with *Reticuloceras gracile*.

When Hull and Green carried out the first serious study of the Namurian rocks about the middle of the nineteenth century they coined the name 'Millstone Grit' in the Peak District for those coarse sandstones or grits, and the intervening shales, which we now recognise as extending from the base of the Kinder Scout Grit upwards to the top of the Rough Rock. They assumed that the base of the Kinder Scout Grit was at a fairly constant horizon. When a lower sandstone developed by thickening in another area it was included in the Kinder Scout Grit, and so the base of the Millstone Grit was lowered. In point of fact many miscorrelations of other sandstone members higher in the Millstone Grit were made. Some of the marine bands had been noticed, but the goniatites had not been studied to such an extent that the evolutionary changes could be used to identify horizons. Such a study did not materialise until 1924 when W. S. Bisat published his epoch-making work on the goniatites of northern England. Since that time the zonal scheme based on goniatites has been improved, and work by geologists of the British Geological Survey and private research workers has gone far to correct correlations and to date Namurian deposits in such a way that it is now safer to synthesise the changing palaeogeography of Namurian time.

It is only with the recent detailed studies of modern sedimentary environments, particularly the fluviatile and the deltaic, that a better understanding of the Namurian sediments is being built up. This is a living example of the basic tenet of geology that the study of the present is the key to the past.

CHAPTER 17

Economic Geology of the Peak District

In previous chapters, economic aspects of the geology of a particular area or formation have been touched on where it has been thought that this would add to a general understanding of the geology; historical facts and traditions have also been included from time to time for the same reason.

GENERAL AND WATER SUPPLY

The economic history of the Peak District has been determined very largely by the geology at least since the time of the Romans. A great deal of the district, especially in the north and west, lies at more than 350m above sea-level. At these heights in midland Britain the temperatures are generally low and the winters can be severe with snow, sometimes heavy, at any time between November and April. Small hill-farms are scattered over much of this country between 350 and 400 metres above sea-level. Pastures are mainly confined to the valleys but further pasture has been won by cultivation of bracken-covered slopes. These farms generally have a few milk cows, pigs and sheep but the conditions are precarious especially as the hay crop from the few meadows may be flattened by heavy rains and windy weather in August. Many of these hill farms have been abandoned and are now in ruins but some have been converted into week-end cottages for people working in the Manchester, Sheffield, and Stoke-on-Trent conurbations. Many a hill farm lies in the lee of a Namurian sandstone scarp where natural springs occur through the pervious sandstone resting directly upon impermeable mudstone and shale. Consequently these farms rarely have water-supply difficulties except during the infrequent summer droughts.

Many hill farms have disappeared as a result of the construction of reservoirs for public water-supply; this applies not only to those occupying ground which has been inundated but also to those on the gathering grounds of the streams and rivers supplying the reservoirs. The reason for the latter is twofold; the problem of disposing of domestic and farm effluent which can not be allowed to drain into stream courses, and the prohibition placed on the keeping of any animals other than sheep in these areas.

Areas which have been depopulated in this way are those around Lamaload Reservoir on the western edge of the Peak District, around Trentabank Reservoir a few kilometres to the south, the upper part of the valley of the River Goyt in connection with the Errwood Reservoir, and around the very large Ladybower Reservoir on the eastern side of the Peak District in which a seven-kilometre length of the valley of the River Derwent has been dammed. In the last case the whole of the village of Derwent was drowned; in 1959, when the water-level was abnormally low, the higher buildings of the old village were visible once again. A long chain of reservoirs occupies a ten-kilometre stretch of the Etherow valley to the north of the Howden moors which are a northerly extension of the Kinder Scout plateau. This valley is also followed by the railway and the main road from Manchester to Penistone and Barnsley or by Stocksbridge to Sheffield.

In the Peak District it is rare to find any trees growing at an altitude exceeding 500m above sea-level. The tree which seems best able to tolerate the conditions normally associated with this kind of altitude is the rowan or mountain ash, known locally as the wicken. At this altitude too, peat tends to be widespread. The author has observed roots and trunks of birch in the basal part of the peat at more than 550m above sea-level. The peat is sometimes as thick as three metres but it is wasting rapidly in many places. The peat-covered hills in the higher Namurian ground are usually referred to as moorland (often abbreviated to 'moors'); they are covered, except in the deep sinuous stream-courses, by a typical suite of plants including heather, bilberry, cotton-grass and rushes. On drier sandstone slopes the rushes are replaced by bracken, while in swampy tracts sphagnum moss is common. Peat has been dug here and there on a small scale for local use as a fuel.

Large areas of peat moorland are given over to grouse-shooting and sheep, apart from acting as gathering-grounds for the numerous reservoirs. The rainfall is fairly high over the moorland areas, an average figure being about one metre a year; the water from the Namurian sandstones is very soft and this property was a major factor in the establishment of the silk industry in Macclesfield on the western fringe of the Peak District. Water from the peat areas has a pale brown colour, and a slightly acid reaction owing to the presence of humic acids from the peat. The effect of these acids is evident where peaty water flows on to limestone, as on the east side of Axe Edge to the south of Buxton; the limestone is etched into strange shapes and its surface assumes a polish.

The Peak District has immense reserves of underground water either from natural subterranean cavities, from mine workings, or from the general body and joint systems in porous rocks.

Natural subterranean cavities are restricted to the limestone area of the Peak District. They include widened joints and natural systems of caverns as around Castleton. The resurgences of Bradwell and Peak's Hole yield almost five million gallons of water a day; this water, which has a fairly high degree of temporary hardness, is pumped to Ladybower Reservoir where it is mixed with the soft slightly acid waters from the generally peaty gathering-grounds.

There are, of course, numerous man-made cavities beneath the limestone country — abandoned lead, zinc, and copper mines, as well as the long drainage-soughs which were constructed in order to lower the water-table to facilitate the winning of ores down to and sometimes below river-level. The major old drainage-levels, sometimes many kilometres in length, include the Stoke Sough which was driven in order to de-water the Ladywash Mine near Eyam, the Moorwood Sough de-watering the Glebe Mine, and the Meerbrook Sough draining old leadmine workings between Cromford and Wirksworth which is reputed to yield between 14 and 19 million gallons of water a day. The water from this sough is hard but considerable volumes are abstracted at the tail of the sough and mixed with soft water from the Namurian sandstones before being added to the public water-supply.

The farms in the limestone area of the Peak District are generally more prosperous than the hill farms of the moorlands of the Namurian. The ground is generally at a lower altitude; and though the soils tend to be thin, mixed farming is the rule. The limestone country is rather dry and many farms have water-supply difficulties. Some must rely almost entirely on rainwater collected in tanks from the roofs of buildings, take water from a river if one is sufficiently near, or transport the water by tanker. Even dew-ponds have to be relied upon in some cases for the watering of cattle. Undoubtedly the driving of soughs in the last two centuries dried up the shallow wells at many farms by lowering the water-table.

Obtaining supplies of underground water by wells and boreholes in the limestone country is rather precarious. If a borehole fails to penetrate major joints in the limestone it may well be dry. In some cases there are perched water-tables where limestone rests upon impermeable basaltic lava or upon wayboards of clay and a number of farms are self-sufficient in water through the possession of a borehole in such a favourable geological location.

In the country occupied by the Namurian and Lower Coal Measures rocks, supplies of underground water can be obtained from boreholes with a considerable measure of success. Above an altitude of about 300m above sea-level the Pleistocene glaciations left little in the way of deposits. On the higher ground the only evidence of glaciation is the occasional erratic boulder, usually of Lake District origin, of a former spill-way, and more indirectly the existence of permafrost conditions to account in part for the form of many dry valleys in the limestone country. Consequently, the outcrops of the Upper Carboniferous sandstones are not covered by a mantle of glacial till or boulder clay, so widespread at lower altitudes, which would impede the percolation of rainwater. Many of these sandstones, especially the Roaches Sandstone, Chatsworth Sandstone, Rough Rock, and Woodhead Hill Sandstone (Crawshaw Sandstone to the east of the Peak District) have a high porosity and well developed joint-systems. They are good aquifers or underground reservoir rocks. Moreover, the water which they yield is generally soft and ideal for textile- and paper-making and other industrial processes as well as for domestic use. The potentialities of these aquifers have not yet been fully exploited, notably because they crop out mainly in those hilly regions where it is more economic to impound surface waters in reservoirs.

In the country of Upper Carboniferous rocks little use is made of water in flooded coal-mine workings, though the village of Kettleshulme on the western fringe of the Peak District obtains its supply from an adit (also known as a 'day-eye' in Lancashire and a 'footrail' or 'footrill' in North Staffordshire) in a coal above the Chatsworth Sandstone or Grit.

Undoubtedly, surface springs were used throughout the Peak District in early days; indeed some springs virtually dictated the location of a number of early settlements. Some springs are still used in villages and others as at Chapel-en-le-Frith and Chinley contribute to the water in reservoirs. Some springs have changed over the centuries; some have run dry owing to the artificial lowering of the water-table or have changed in character. A short distance to the east of Barmoor Clough, in the north-west corner of the limestone outcrop and on the south side of the Chapel-en-le-Frith to Castleton road, is the Ebbing and Flowing Well. As a boy, the author witnessed the action of ebbing and flowing, presumably due to some kind of siphoning in the joints of the limestone, but today this action has ceased and the flow of water has diminished considerably.

MINING

In earlier chapters considerable reference has been made to the mining of ores of lead, zinc, and copper, especially in the areas of Castleton, Eyam, Matlock, Winster, Wirksworth, Youlgreave, and Ecton in the valley of the River Manifold. The ore bodies occur as vertical veins or rakes, flats, pipes, and irregular masses. The limestone area, particularly on its northern and eastern sides, is cut by numerous rakes the general trend of which lies between E–W and NE–SW. Some carry quaint names such as Shuttle Rake, Maiden Rake and Odin Vein.

Mention has already been made of the historic local customs and regulations relating to the mining of metalliferous ores in Derbyshire. There is a very extensive literature referring to lead-mines and mining in this country, and readers wishing to follow this up will find a few of the more important references in the Bibliography; in these will be found much more extensive references to this fascinating subject.

Undoubtedly extensive reserves of galena still remain not only at deeper levels beneath parts of the limestone area, but also in concealed areas to the north and east where the limestone is covered by Namurian rocks. In the Matlock and Ashover district a considerable amount of exploratory work has been carried out beneath this cover; some ore was got, but old workings were encountered and it is clear that even in some of these concealed areas the reserves will have to be sought at depth.

Since the closing of the Mill Close Mine near Matlock there have been no lead-mines working in the Peak District. At the present time the Cavendish Mill near Eyam which processes fluor-spar from Ladywash Mine and from opencast workings on Longstone Edge has a lead concentrate by-product from the flotation of the fluor-spar.

Barytes is also produced as a by-product at the Cavendish Mill. This mineral has a number of uses, the most important one being as a filler in the paper industry. It was formerly employed for giving 'body' to paints, but its importance in this connexion is diminishing with the increasing production of synthetic paints. There is also a growing demand for barytes (also known as 'heavy spar' on account of its high specific gravity) now that there is an extensive drilling programme for methane beneath the bed of the North Sea. Ground barytes is a useful additive in the production of heavy drilling-muds used in the drilling of boreholes through the rocks encountered there. Some barytes is also produced by the reworking of old mine spoil-heaps or 'hillocks' in the northern part of the limestone area where it is one of the common gangue minerals associated with galena.

Another gangue mineral in this association in the north and north-eastern parts of the limestone country is fluor-spar or fluorite. Many of the old mine-hillocks have been or are being reworked in order to pick out the fluor-spar. When the old lead-mines were working, fluor-spar was a worthless gangue, but it is now important as a flux in the steel industry, particularly around Sheffield, and in the production of hydrofluoric acid. It has already been noticed that fluor-spar is currently being mined at the Ladywash Mine and worked in open works on Longstone Edge.

Coal has also been mined in the Upper Carboniferous rocks on the western side of the Peak District, but apart from one or two very small concerns on Ludworth Moor about five kilometres south-west of Glossop none is being raised today.

The General Strike in Britain in 1926 led to the opening of many small mines down the western fringe of the Peak District from Glossop southwards to Macclesfield, and many previously untouched outcrops were exploited usually by the driving of adits into the seams.

A coal in the Namurian above the Chatsworth Sandstone and below the *Gastrioceras cancellatum* marine band, known in the Glossop area as the Simmondley Coal, had been worked many years ago around Glossop and Hayfield. This coal had also been worked during the last century at Danebower Colliery alongside the Buxton–Congleton road about seven kilometres south-west of Buxton. The coal was about one metre in thickness and fairly clean. In 1926 the author was able to examine a little mine in this coal, known as Penny Hole, close to Orchard Farm to the east of Three Shires Bridge. The coal was almost one metre thick; an uncrushed internal mould of *Calamites* was found in an upright position in the seam, an example worth mentioning because macro-fossils are rarely found in coal.

Coals in the Lower Coal Measures have been worked at Thornset near Hayfield; around Marple and Mellor; near Taxal, in the valley of the River Goyt; and on Goyt's Moss and Goldsitch Moss, both in the axial region of the Goyt Syncline. These coals were generally thin and either shaly or sulphurous, and it is thought that most of the coal extracted was used in lime-burning in Derbyshire.

Associated usually with the mining of the Goyt Syncline coals has been the exploitation of some of the seat-earths, both fireclays and ganisters for the production of firebricks and furnace hearths. Usually the thickest fireclay, about two metres thick, is that beneath the thin coal underlying the *Gastrioceras subcrenatum* marine band. The coal itself is usually too thin for working; it is known as the Six-inch Mine on the western side of the Peak District and as the Pot Clay Coal on the eastern side towards Sheffield.

QUARRYING

The Peak District has been the scene of quarrying for centuries. Immense amounts of rock are present in the dry-stone walls which are such a characteristic feature of the Peak District scene, be it on the Namurian moors where the walls of sandstone have weathered to dark grey or black or on the limestone where the white-weathering walls sometimes enclose extraordinarily narrow strip-fields. Most of the walling-stone was obtained by opening small quarries more or less on the spot. As a result the change from sandstone walls to limestone walls marks the approximate boundary between the Upper and Lower Carboniferous.

Almost every kind of rock has been or is being quarried; limestone, shale, basalt, dolerite, and sandstone.

Immense quantities of limestone have been removed from the Peak District limestone area. It is a rule that farms and houses are built or faced with limestone. However, the greatest amounts were quarried in the past for lime-burning, when the lime was so important an ingredient of mortar and when it was widely used in agriculture. Scores of quarries working many horizons, but concentrated generally in the purer limestones of the D_1 zone, had their own limekilns. Today the limestone quarries are fewer but larger. The Tunstead Quarry in Great Rocks Dale about eight kilometres east of Buxton has a face over forty metres in height and nearly two kilometres in length. It is probably the longest limestone quarry-face in Europe. The limestone is used in the alkali industry centred on Northwich in Cheshire; it is employed as ground limestone for agricultural purposes, and some goes for aggregate and roadstone.

The limestone worked in Great Rocks Dale is part of the Chee Tor Beds of the D_1 zone. It has a high degree of purity, the calcium carbonate in some thick beds being as high as 99 per cent. For over a century these limestones have produced 'best Buxton lime'.

The Chee Tor Beds are a great national asset and it is clear that these limestones must be conserved for use in those industrial and agricultural processes where less pure limestones would not suffice. Nowadays, because much of the limestone country falls within the Peak District National Park, it is becoming increasingly difficult to obtain the necessary planning permission to open new quarries. In an area of such great natural beauty this, without doubt, is a good thing.

Limestone is also used in the production of cement. Earle's Cement Works at Hope to the east of Castleton uses limestones high in the D_2 zone. Chert is present in these beds but measures are adopted very successfully to control the total silica content. Close by, Namurian shales are quarried for the other essential ingredient of cement. In a similar way the juxtaposition of suitable limestones and shales is used to produce cement near Waterhouses to the south of Leek, Staffordshire.

The basalt of the lava flows in the Miller's Dale and Matlock areas has been quarried on a relatively small scale for roadstone. The intrusive dolerites on the other hand, being more durable, having a higher crushing-strength, and lacking the amygdales of the lavas (toadstones) have been exploited on a large scale at Waterswallows to the north-east of Buxton where the dolerite is in the form of a very thick sill, and at Calton Hill almost ten kilometres east of Buxton where an olivine dolerite was intruded through Lower Carboniferous lavas in Westphalian time. Dolerite quarries of lesser importance occur in the Matlock and Bonsall areas.

Almost all the quarries especially in the limestones are highly mechanised and very little material is now got by hand. Holes are drilled in line a few metres behind the face, charges are put in the holes and these are detonated simultaneously by remote control. The broken material is then carried to the crushers and screens by specially designed heavy vehicles.

Nearly all the sandstone formations in the Peak District have been quarried. Because of the regional structure they are necessarily confined to the peripheral areas. In the Namurian, the Kinder Scout Sandstone or Grit, Roaches Sandstone, Chatsworth Sandstone, and Rough Rock have all been worked. Prior to World War II sandstones and other rocks were used for many things which today are made of cement and concrete. They were employed in buildings internally for staircases, floors and decoration; roads were lined with stone kerbs, town streets were made with stone blocks or 'setts' and pavements were constructed with flags of sandstone. Bridges incorporated a great deal of rock and railway station platforms were of natural flags. All around the Peak District small quarries in Namurian or Lower Coal Measures sandstones were producing these materials. The author's impression of one of these quarries is shown on p 133.

Today only a few sandstone quarries are still working around the Peak District; some are producing pulp-stones for export to Norway and Sweden, others are making special grindstones for use in the steel industry. Here and there, a small quarry is turning out lumps of sandstone for garden rockeries or irregular pieces of flaggy sandstone for crazy paving.

To the geologist, attempting to decipher the history of the Peak District by studying its minerals, rocks, and fossils, quarries old and new are invaluable for the geological evidence which they afford.

Glossary

ANHYDRITE — An anhydrous form of calcium sulphate, $CaSO_4$. Along with rock-salt (Halite) NaCl, gypsum $CaSO_{4.2}H_2O$ and several less frequnet minerals, it is one of a group of evaporites formed by the evaporation of sea-water, and its presence often indictates the existence of shallow partly-locked seas in arid regions.

ARENACEOUS — Sandy, applied to rocks such as sandstones of all kinds and certain siltstones.

ARGILLACEOUS — composed predominantly of clay minerals, but besides being used to describe groups of sediments can also be used for some metamorphic rocks such as certain types of slates.

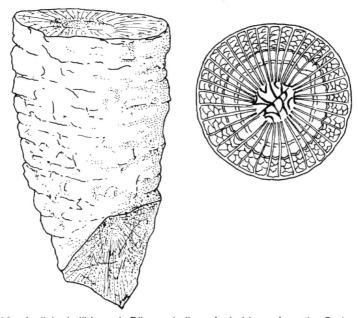

Fig 80 A clisiophyllid coral, *Dibunophyllum* cf. *derbiense* from the Carboniferous Limestone (D₂ zone), Bakewell, Derbyshire. Natural size. Notice the 'stick-insect'-like arrangement of vertical plates in the central area of the corallum in the thin-section

AUGITE — a common pyroxene mineral $(CaMgFeAl)_2$ $(AlSi)_2O_6$ found in many basic volcanic and plutonic rocks.

AUTHIGENIC — applied to a mineral which has grown as an independent crystallographic entity in a sedimentary rock.

BRECCIA — a consolidated rock composed of large angular fragments as opposed to the rounded ones which make up a conglomerate. Many breccias are consolidated scree deposits. Fault breccias are broken angular fragments occurring along fault planes which have been bound together subsequently by the deposition of minerals such as calcite and quartz.

BRUCITE — a magnesium mineral with the composition $Mg(OH)_2$ found in thermally metamorphosed dolomitic limestones.

CALCAREOUS — containing calcium usually as calcium carbonate. Apart from limestones, may be applied to mudstones and sandstones which have a cement of calcium carbonate or contain a noticeable quantity of shell debris.

CLISIOPHYLLID CORAL — a general term used in this work for simple Lower Carboniferous rugose corals, like *Clisiophyllum*, which are cylindrical in shape, have a regular outer zone of dissepiments, and a wide axial structure with thin septal lamellae abutting on to a short median plate (Figure 80).

CROSS-BEDDING — partings oblique to the bedding planes usually in sands and sandstones, more rarely in limestones. The best examples occur in wind-blown or aeolian sands, but many sands deposited in rivers or in deltas show well marked cross-bedding. Cross-bedding bears a definite relation to the direction of flow in the medium and consequently, in the case of an ancient sand, is a useful criterion for determining palaeo-current direction.

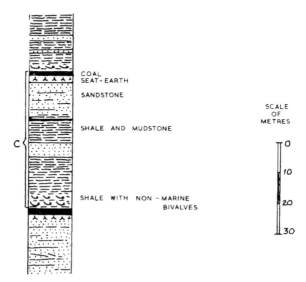

Fig 81   A typical cyclotherm (c) in the Coal Measures

Fig 82   A disconformity; its position at the surface is marked by the tree. Note the parallelism of beds above and below the disconformity

CRUST — the outer spherical zone of the Earth, composed of rocks with specific gravities of 2.5 to 3.4, having a variable lower limit (fixed at a seismic discontinuity called the Mohorovicic or M-discontinuity) depending upon whether continent or ocean lies upon the surface. An average thickness for the crust would be about ten kilometres.

CYCLOTHEM — A complete cycle of sedimentation involving two or more lithologies (Figure 81).

DETRITAL — composed of broken or comminuted material.

DIP — the angle measured in degrees between the bedding planes in a sediment and the horizontal. The complete description of the dip of rocks involves the direction as well as the amount. The inclination of a fault plane from the horizontal is the dip of the fault, but it is more usual to state the hade, the angle in degrees between the fault plane and the vertical.

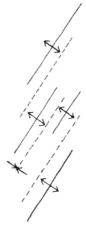

Fig 83   Fold axes showing an approximate *en échelon* arrangement

DISCONFORMITY — a type of unconformity in which the strata above the break have the same dip and strike as those below. A disconformity is usually marked by a conspicuous bedding-plane showing evidence of pene-contemporaneous erosion (Figure 82).

DYKE SWARM — a large collection of igneous dykes showing either approximate parallelism or a radial relationship.

EN ÉCHELON — applied to structures, mainly folds, which are parallel but off-set (Figure 83).

FAULT — a fracture in the rocks along which movement has taken place. The rocks which have moved relatively downwards are said to be on the downthrow side; the upthrow side of the fault is that on which the rocks have been displaced relatively upwards. A normal fault dips or hades towards the downthrow side, while in a reverse fault the fault hades towards the upthrow side. In a tear- or wrench-fault the displacement is essentially in a horizontal direction (Figure 84).

GRADED BEDDING — a sedimentary unit showing a sorting according to grain size with the largest grains at the base and the smallest or finest at the top.

HEAD — an unconsolidated deposit formed by the process of solifluction, soil and sub-soil moving downhill under the action of gravity, aided by successive freezing and thawing.

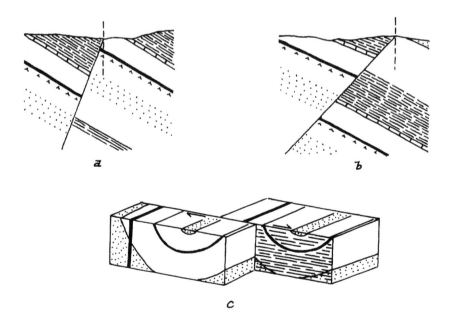

Fig 84   Diagrammatic sections of faults: a, normal fault; b, reverse fault; c, tear or wrench fault

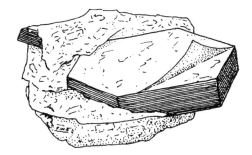

Fig 85   A crystal ('book') of muscovite or white mica showing perfect cleavage parallel to a crystal face. Natural size

LACUSTRINE — pertaining to lakes, hence lacustrine clays, deposits, etc.

MAGMA — the heated liquid material from which igneous rocks, both intrusive and extrusive, are formed. A magma can be imagined as a highly heated porridge-like mass which may be granular through the separating out of minerals the freezing points of which are higher than that of the magma at a given time. When magma reaches the surface gaseous products (volatiles) are given off, sometimes explosively, and lava issues from the orifice.

MAGNETITE — a magnetic iron oxide, Fe_3O_4.

MINERAL CLEAVAGE — the property possessed by many minerals of splitting in a predetermined direction or directions. Rock-salt or halite cubic crystals cleave in three directions parallel to the crystal faces; in fluorite cubic crystals the cleavage is in four directions across the corners of the cubes or parallel to the faces of an octahedron. Some minerals of which quartz is the most common do not possess any cleavage. Cleavage or lack of it is often a useful distinguishing characteristic (Figure 85).

MINERAL HARDNESS — a physical property which can be useful in the determination of mineral species. The hardness of a mineral can be determined by reference to Mohs' Scale which uses ten minerals placed according to their relative hardnesses as follows:

1	Talc	6	Orthoclase feldspar
2	Gypsum	7	Quartz
3	Calcite	8	Topaz
4	Fluorite	9	Corundum
5	Apatite	10	Diamond

NEPTUNIAN DYKE — A submarine fissure which has been filled with marine sediments from above.

NODULE — A discrete spherical, ovoid or sometimes irregular mass of ironstone, chert, etc found in clays, seat-earths, mudstones, shales and limestones. Many nodules have formed around organic nuclei during post-depositional changes in sediments.

OLIVINE — a group of iron magnesium silicate minerals lying between pure iron silicate (fayalite, Fe_2SiO_4) and pure magnesium silicate (forsterite, Mg_2SiO_4). Olivine

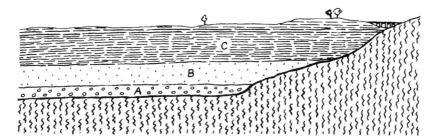

Fig 86 Overlap of one formation by another. The series A, B, C rest unconformably upon an old land surface. Successively younger beds come to lie directly upon this surface. C overlaps B, and A is overlapped by B

decomposes to produce serpentine and iron oxide.

ORTHOCLASE — A potash feldspar, potassium aluminium silicate, $KAlSI_3O_8$, pink or white in colour. An essential mineral of granites.

OVERLAP — In the course of a marine transgression on to a land area later sediments extend farther landwards than earlier sediments. The earlier sediments are said to be overlapped by the later ones. The phenomenon is called overlap (Figure 86).

PLAGIOCLASE — a group of soda-lime feldspars ranging from albite, sodium aluminium silicate, at one extreme, to anorthite, calcium aluminium silicate, at the other.

PLUNGE — the angle between the horizontal and the crest or trough of a fold in the

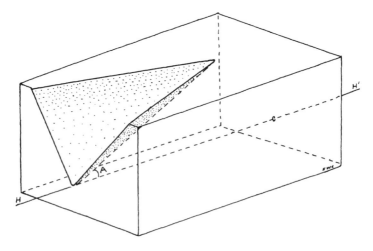

Fig 87 A plunging syncline. HH' is a horizontal line, A is the angle of plunge. Notice the V-shaped outcrop of the bed on the upper (plane) surface

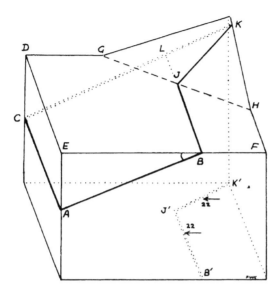

Fig 88 Strike of a bed. The bed AB dips to the left at the angle ABE. The outcrop AC on the vertical face is horizontal: AC is the direction of strike of the bed. Notice that on the upper plane surface the outcrop of the bed follows the direction of strike. Along the line GH the ground rises and the outcrop of the bed beyond J extends to K so that the direction of outcrop there departs widely from the direction of its strike. The outcrop is also shown projected vertically on to the base of the block at B'J'K'

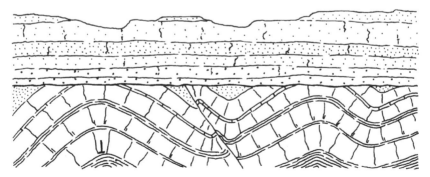

Fig 89 An angular unconformity. The horizontal beds above rest unconformably upon folded and faulted beds below

direction of the axis of the fold (Figure 87).

QUAQUAVERSAL DIP — radially-directed inward or outward dips in structural basins or domes; sometimes also applied to such dips in limestone reefs where they are depositional or original dips.

SLICKENSIDES — an old mining term applied to the striations found on faulted surfaces; they indicate the most recent direction of movement along the fault.

STRIKE — a direction at right angles to the dip of a bed. A road driven in a dipping coal seam in a direction normal to the dip would be horizontal (Figure 88).

TURBIDITY CURRENT — a high-velocity submarine current flowing down the continental slope into the abyssal depths; such currents have a high density owing to the sediment picked up and can carry shallow-water sediments into deep marine environments. The sediments laid down by turbidity currents show a number of diagnostic characteristics. They are referred to generally as turbidites.

THIN-SECTION — a slice of a mineral, rock, or fossil about 0.025mm thick mounted on a microscope slide and protected by a cover-slip, the mounting medium being canada balsam, lakeside cement, or an epoxy resin.

UNCONFORMITY — a major stratigraphical break. An angular unconformity involves two series of sediments with different amounts of dip and in all probability varying directions of strike (Figure 89).

Selected Bibliography

Aitkenhead, N., Chisholm, J. I. & Stevenson, I. P., 1985. Geology of the country around Buxton, Leek and Bakewell, *Memoir British Geological Survey*. (1:50,000 geological Sheet 111)

Arnold-Bemrose, H. H., 1907. The Toadstones of Derbyshire; their field Relations and Petrography. *Quarterly Journal Geological Society London*, vol. 63

British Museum (Natural History). 1969. British Palaeozoic Fossils.

Butcher, N. J. D. & Ford, T. D., 1973. The Carboniferous Limestone of Monsal Dale, Derbyshire. *Mercian Geologist*, vol. 4.

Cope, F. W., 1933. A tholeiite Dyke near Buxton, Derbyshire. *Geological Magazine*, vol. LXX

Cope, F. W., 1946. Intraformational contorted rocks in the Upper Carboniferous of the Southern Pennines. *Quarterly Journal Geological Society London*, vol. 101

Cope, F. W., 1949. Correlation of the Coal Measures of Macclesfield and the Goyt Trough. *Transactions Institute Mining Engineers*, vol. 108.

Cope, F. W., 1979. The age of the volcanic rocks in the Woo Dale Borehole, Derbyshire. *Geological Magazine*, vol. 116

Cope, F. W., 1998. The Peak District. Geologists' Association Guide No. (In press)

Evans, W. B., Wilson, A. A., Taylor, B. J. & Price, D., 1968. Geology of the country around Macclesfield, Congleton, Crewe and Middlewich. *Memoir British Geological Survey*. (1:63,360 geological Sheet 110)

Ford, T. D., 1996. Geology of Castleton. *Geologists' Association Guide*, No. 56

Ford, T. D. & Rievwerts, J. H., 1968. *Lead Mining in the Peak District*. Peak Park Planning Board.

George, T. N., Johnson, G. A. L., Mitchell, M., Prentice, J. E., Ramsbottom, W. H. C., Sevastopulo, G. D. & Wilson, R. B., 1976. Dinantian (Lower Carboniferous). A correlation of Dinantian rocks in the British Isles. *Geological Society*, Special Report No. 7.

Ramsbottom, W. H. C., 1973. Transgressions and regressions in the Dinantian, a new synthesis of British Dinantian Stratigraphy. *Proceedings Yorkshire Geological Society*, vol. 39.

Read, H. H., 1962. Rutley's Elements of Mineralogy.

Shirley, J., 1959. The Carboniferous Limestone of the Monyash–Wirksworth area, Derbyshire. *Quarterly Journal Geological Society London*, vol. 114.

Smith, E. G., Rhys, G. H. & Eden, R. A., 1967. Geology of the country around Chesterfield, Matlock and Mansfield. *Memoir British Geological Survey*. (1:63,360 geological Sheet 112)

Stevenson, I. P. & Gaunt, G. D., 1971. Geology of the country around Chapel-en-le-Frith. *Memoir British Geological Survey*. (1:63,360 geological Sheet 99)

Tomkeieff, S. J., 1928. The volcanic complex of Calton Hill, Derbyshire. *Quarterly Journal Geological Society*, vol. 84.

Vaughan, A., 1905. The palaentological, sequence in the Carboniferous Limestone of the Bristol area. *Quarterly Journal Geological Society*, vol. 61.

The maps and memoirs of the British Geological Survey, published by HM Stationery Office, are particularly reliable and informative sources of information. The maps are on the scale of 1:50,000 or in some cases 1:63,360, whilst for some selected areas (Buxton, Castleton, Miller's Dale, Monyash, and The Roaches) they are available on thes cale of 1:25,000. The memoirs carry much local detail and extensive bibliographies which will prove invaluable to readers wishing to follow up particular aspects of the geology of the area.

Appendix I

Subdivisions of geological time with approximate durations and ages

Era	Approximate age (in years)	Period	Approximate duration (in years)	Cenozoic Epoch
CENOZOIC		QUATERNARY	10,000	*RECENT
			2M	*PLEISTOCENE
	2M		5M	*PLIOCENE
	7M		19M	*MIOCENE
	26M	TERTIARY	12M	OLIGOCENE
	38M		16M	EOCENE
	54M		10M	PALAEOCENE
	64M	CRETACEOUS	71M	
MESOZOIC	135M	JURASSIC	57M	
	192M	*TRIASSIC	33M	
	225M	*PERMIAN	55M	
	280M	*CARBONIFEROUS	80M	
	360M	DEVONIAN	80M	
PALAEOZOIC	410M	SILURIAN	30M	
	440M	*ORDOVICIAN	90M	
	530M	CAMBRIAN	40M	
	570M			
PRECAMBRIAN ERAS		Worldwide subdivisions not yet well established	4,000M	

Notes:
1. M = 1,000,000 years.
2. Oldest terrestrial rock dated up to present has an age of approximately 3,990M years.
3. Age of Earth is at least 4,500M years.
4. The Lower Carboniferous represents about 20M years.
5. In North America the Carboniferous System is replaced by two distinct systems, the older being the Mississippian the younger the Pennsylvanian. The boundary between these systems falls into the lowest part of the British Upper Carboniferous.
* Rocks of these ages are present in the Peak District and its fringe areas at outcrop or proved in boreholes.

189

Appendix II

		Bivalves (non-marine lamellibranchs)	Goniatites (Zones)	Corals/Brachiopods (Zones)
UPPER CARBONIFEROUS	Stephanian	*Anthraconaia prolifera*		
	Westphalian (Coal Measures)	*Anthraconauta tenuis* *Anthraconauta phillipsii* *Anthracosia similis* and *Anthraconaia pulchra* *Anthraconaia modiolaris* *Carbonicola communis* *Anthraconaia lenisulcata*	*Anthracoceras* sp	
	Namurian		*Gastrioceras* G_2 *Gastrioceras* G_1 *Reticuloceras* R_2 R_1 *Homoceras* H_2 H_1 *Eumorphoceras* E_2 E_1	

LOWER CARBONIFEROUS (DINANTIAN)

Series	Genus zone	Zone	Former coral-brach. zones	Stages
Visean	Goniatites	P_2		
		P_1	D_2	Brigantian
		B_2	D_1	Asbian
	Beyrichoceras	B_1	S_2	
			C_2S_1	Holkerian
Tournaisian	Pericyclues		C_1	
			Z_2	
			Z_1	Chadian
	Gattendorfia		K_2	
			K_1	Courceyan

Note: K = *Cleistopora* (now *Vaughania* owing to re-definition of genera), Z = *Zaphrentis*, C = *Caninia*, S = *Seminula* (now *Composita* owing to re-definition of genera), D = *Dibuno-phyllum*.

Appendix III

THE CARBONIFEROUS ROCKS AS DEVELOPED IN
THE PEAK DISTRICT

	Major subdivision	Maximum thickness	Main rock types
UPPER CARBONIFEROUS	Westphalian ('Coal Measures')	300m (950ft)	Shale and mudstone, sandstone, fireclay, coal
UPPER CARBONIFEROUS	Namurian ('Millstone Grit')	1250m (4,000ft)	Sandstone, shale and mudstone
LOWER CARBONIFEROUS	Dinantian ('Carboniferous Limestone')	2100m (6,850ft)	Limestone, shale and mudstone, basalt, chert

Evidence from boreholes has been taken into account in computing the thickness of the Dinantian rocks.

Appendix IV

THE DINANTIAN SUCCESSION EXPOSED IN THE WYE VALLEY, DERBYSHIRE, AND PROVED IN THE WOO DALE BOREHOLE

Name of formation	Zone	Stage	Approximate thickness (metres)	Notes on fossils, lithologies, etc
Ashford Beds	P_2		40	*Goniatites granosum* near top
Monsal Dale Beds	D_2		150	White Cliff Coral Band in lower half Litton Tuff near base
Priestcliffe Beds	D_2	Br	36	Thick light coloured limestones passing eastwards into dark beds with chert containing Hobs House Coral Band
Upper Lava			up to 40	
Station Quarry Beds	D_2		10	Marked disconformity at base
Miller's Dale Beds	D_1		40	*Palaeosmilia murchisoni* abundant near top
Lower Lava		As	up to 25	
Chee Tor Beds	D_1		100–130	*Davidsonina septosa* band near top
Woo Dale Beds	S_2	Ho	100	*Daviesiella llangollensis* and *Davidsonina carbonaria* of sporadic occurrence
Beds proved in Woo Dale borehole	C_2S_1		274	*Davidsonina carbonaria, Dorlodotia briati* and foraminifera suggesting basal Viséan

Note: Zone (coral-brachiopod) C = *Caninia*, S = Seminula, D = *Dibunophyllum*.
Stage; Ho = Holkerian, As = Asbian, Br = Brigantian

Appendix V

Zone	WESTPHALIAN
	Gastrioceras subcrenatum
Gastrioceras G_1	*G. cumbriense*
Reticuloceras R_2	*R. superbilingue*
R_1	*R. reticulatum*
Homoceras H_2	*Homoceratoides prereticulatus*
H_1	*Homoceras beyrichianum*
Eumorphoceras E_2	*Nuculoceras nuculum*
E_1	*Cravenoceras malhamense*
	Cravenoceras leion
	DINANTIAN

Note:

1 The base of the Namurian is at the *Cravenoceras leion* horizon. (= base of E_1 zone).

2 The *Gastrioceras subcrenatum* marine band is at the base of the G_2 Zone which is also the base of the Westphalian (Coal Measures).

193

Appendix VI

CORRELATION OF BRACHIOPOD/CORAL AND GONIATITE/BIVALVE ZONAL SCHEMES

Zone on Shelf or Massif			*Zone in Reef (and/or Basin)*
Upper *Posidonia*	P_2 (part)	P_2	Upper *Posidonia*
Upper *Dibunophyllum*	D_2	P_1	Lower *Posidonia*
Lower *Dibunophyllum*	D_1	B_2	Upper *Beyrichoceras*
Seminula	S_2	B_1	Lower *Beyrichoceras*

Appendix VII

DINANTIAN SUCCESSION IN THE DOVE DALE AREA

Zone	*Formations*
P_1	Hollington End Beds in basin (other facies not seen)
D_1 (B_2)	Gag Lane Limestone in the basin, Narrowdale Limestone (reef) in the marginal area, and Alsop Moor Limestone on the massif.
$S_1–S_2$	Manifold Limestone-with-Shales in the basin, Alstonfield Limestone (reef) in the marginal area, and Wolfscote Dale Limestone on the massif.
$C_1–C_2$	Milldale Limestone in the basin, Dove Dale Limestone (reef) in the marginal area, and Iron Tors Limestone on the massif.

194

Index

195

Field Notes

FIELD NOTES

FIELD NOTES

GEOLOGY EXPLAINED IN THE PEAK DISTRICT

FIELD NOTES